The Compassion Remedy

Catherine W. Schweikert, PhD

The Compassion Remedy

How to leverage the
psychophysiological benefits
of compassion to beat burnout,
renew relationships,
and enjoy greater well-being

WORLDCHANGERS
MEDIA

Hardcover ISBN: 978-1-955811-36-1
Paperback ISBN: 978-1-955811-37-8
E-book ISBN: 978-1-955811-38-5
LCCN: 2023905475

First hardcover edition: July 2023

Cover design: Michael Rehder www.rehderandcompanie.com
Layout and typesetting: Bryna Haynes
Editors: Stephen Nathans-Kelly, Bryna Haynes, Paul Baillie-Lane

Published by WorldChangers Media
PO Box 83, Foster, RI 02825
www.WorldChangers.Media

To my fellow compassion ambassador, David Breaux,
the "Compassion Guy," Davis, California.
May you rest in power, peace, and compassion.

Praise

"Expertly written, insightful and timely, *The Compassion Remedy* is a masterclass on the necessity of compassion in our lives and in the healthcare system. Combining evidence-based research and personal stories, Catherine gives us a step-by-step guide how to increase compassion in ourselves, toward our patients and everyone around us." - **James R. Doty, MD, founder and director, the Center for Compassion and Altruism Research and Education at Stanford University, senior editor of the** *Oxford Handbook of Compassion Science***, and author of the** *New York Times* **bestseller,** *Into the Magic Shop: A Neurosurgeon's Quest to Discover the Mysteries of the Brain and the Secrets of the Heart*

"Catherine eloquently describes what compassion truly is, both philosophically and physiologically, and guides the reader to find what it means and how it feels to them personally. As a psychophysiologist, I appreciate the need for this book now while people cope with one of the largest existential moments in the history of human emotion." - **Cynthia Kerson, 2(PhD), QEEGD, BCN, BCB Senior Fellow, BCB-HRV Associate Professor, Saybrook University, Department of Applied Psychophysiology**

"This book is a must-read! Catherine gives compassion new life grounded in practical application. Her evidence- based research and storytelling illuminate why compassion is accessible and imperative for all." - **Neelama Eyres, Co-Founder and Director, Applied Compassion Training™ (CCARE) at Stanford University**

"Compassion is the cure! I, like many, trained in an environment where compassion was viewed as a potential weakness. It was good if carefully reined and was a potential source of weakness; it would prevent the objectivity that modern medicine demands. Along my journey, there have been those that reject the vilifying of compassion and created a space for my own compassion to survive and grow. I have had the good fortune to work alongside Catherine Schweikert for a decade, where she has helped maintain a safe place for compassion in my practice and life. Now, you, too can benefit from her spirit, and learn the evolving knowledge of the scientific basis and personal value of compassion." - **Steven Vilter, MD**

Table of Contents

Introduction

IN MARCH OF 2020, we closed the doors to our urgent care center in Sacramento for people with respiratory symptoms and began seeing them outside on our rooftop parking lot. Their cars became our exam rooms. Physically, we had a ten-by-ten-foot canopy to guard our computers from the elements, limited PPE, and even more limited testing for the COVID-19 virus. Emotionally, we had fear, anger, confusion, and a desperate desire to help everyone we could.

I remember seeing the line of cars span from the fourth floor down to the first floor of the building. I remember doing what we could for as many patients as we could, leaning inside their car windows and listening to their lungs. Reassurance was our primary prescription.

Each day we would test as many as we could for COVID—until our limited supply of tests ran out. At the beginning of each shift, I would ask how many tests we had for the day; the answer would usually be five or six. Sometimes, on really lucky days, we might have twenty.

No matter how many tests we had, it was never enough. The number of patients with respiratory symptoms who wanted us to test them for the virus that was killing so many people ranged from fifty to more than a hundred a day. We could not keep up. This was unheard of in our modern age of medicine. We could only test those who had the highest risk of dying from COVID—as if anyone knew who that was in those early days. All others were turned away without tests. At times, this meant denying even those with the highest risk, because we ran out of testing swabs prior to their arrival.

We treated our patients as best we could, often not knowing the outcomes or cause. I recall the pleading voices of my patients and their fearful eyes. For the first time in twenty years of practicing medicine, I felt *completely* ineffective, and frankly scared. I was not alone; many of us felt this way. Some of those who worked through the earliest HIV infections remembered this overwhelm and panic well, along with the fear and uncertainty. Unfortunately, whatever lessons of tenderness and compassion we, as a profession, learned in the 1980s did not translate to current day. Those who had been practicing medicine in the '80s had already survived the unthinkable; the rest of us were just getting started.

I felt like the caring needed was too big for me to hold. I felt like I needed to shut down aspects of my compassionate self to survive. I was wrong.

Looking back, I've often wondered what that experience would have been like if I had known then what I know now. If we could have harnessed the energy of compassion—and self-compassion—in those tumultuous first few weeks, at a time when just getting through each shift was a struggle in itself, would there have been less burnout? Fewer resignations, retirements, and reassignments? Less judgment, blaming, fear-mongering, and anger?

A growing body of research on compassion has revealed the benefits of this sometimes elusive, yet necessary, quality of being, and nowhere is the need for greater compassion more evident than in the medical field in times of crisis.

At the time, "experts" were telling us that the virus was not airborne. However, those of us on the front lines knew better. We knew it was airborne, and we knew we needed to take precautions beyond those already recommended to stop it from spreading. That was how we made the decision to take our clinic outside: to give ourselves and our patients some measure of protection, because we didn't have adequate PPE and we did not know how virulent this virus was. We also didn't know how to treat the disease, and we did not have any prior experience to help us anticipate or deal with what would come next.

After the first twenty or so patients with COVID symptoms arrived in their cars—often in the first hour of each shift—the rest of the day became a blur. I know my colleagues felt much the same way. I would come home at night absolutely exhausted and terrified that I would bring the virus home to my family. I worried that my husband and my son would get sick and die because of me.

In those early days, we kept trying to reassure one another that everything was going to be okay. *We've got this.* We continued to try to help each other feel safe, to comfort our colleagues, patients, and ourselves as best we could. That was as close to compassion as we could get.

When one of us would come down with COVID, it was eerie. Like somehow it was more wrong for us to catch it. We were trying to help; we should have been "protected." When it started to take down one of our own, we found it harder to be patient. Harder to be kind. Harder to come to work. We did not speak of compassion; there was too much fear.

When one of my colleagues ended up on a respirator, the rest of us were terrified. We knew how many never made it back from that. Powerlessness is not something we are used to in this profession. Yet, powerless we were.

Driving home after each shift, I would listen to the same CD in my car: May Erlewine's *Mother Lion*. These lines from "Shake the World" still take me right back to that time:

I wanna let love in, I don't want to fear it
And if I'm going to give it my all, I want you to hear it
I wanna shake the world

I would sing along and cry all the way home, hoping that some benevolent force would hear me: *Protect me and those I love, protect and care for us all.* I made my makeshift solid ground with music and routine.

When I arrived home from each shift and entered through the back gate of my home, I would start taking off my clothes on the back porch. Naked, I would carry my clothes to the laundry room. Immediately, I'd throw them into the washer on the "sanitize" setting. Then I would seal those clothes away in a bag until my next shift. I would tell my husband and son to go away and not come near me as I rushed to the shower, and then I would scrub my skin hard until it turned a bright red and wash my hair until I felt safe. Sometimes this would take a few minutes. Sometimes it would take over an hour.

Every single time I went to work for two years, I wore a core uniform. In summer, the heat underneath the tent in the parking lot could become unbearable, so I wore a blue sleeveless T-shirt under the light blue, plastic-bag PPE we had at the time. In the winter, I wore a hospital-assigned black jacket over the blue sleeveless shirt, and the rest remained the same: a pair of scrubs from my first job in a hospital. The "October 2001" printed on the back pocket reminded me that I'd made it this far.

I also had a pair of socks printed with a picture of my

son's face. In the picture, he had safety goggles on; he'd been pretending he was a scientist. His face reminded me of my incredible family waiting for me at home. Most of all, it was my son I was trying to protect. I felt strong and capable when I looked down at my socks and saw his beautiful face. An unintended effect was that seeing the socks and my son's face humanized me in the eyes of my patients.

Last, but certainly not least, I had a pair of underwear with owls printed on them. Over the last few years, owls have come to represent to me the ancient wisdom of my ancestors and Ma—the grandmother who raised me, and who passed away in 2017.

Superstitions became completely reasonable, and I held them in a sacred way. I felt that if I just kept these clothes on every time I came to work, not only would they protect me, but they would also remind me of my years of experience, of Ma's love and support, and of my reasons for living: my son and my husband. I kept these reminders with me *every single shift*.

I was able to stop wearing this one particular outfit once we were able to adequately test, treat, and vaccinate every patient that needed it, but this did not happen until 2022. I still keep those clothes in my work bag and bring them with me to every shift that I work.

Throughout it all, and especially in those terrifying and chaotic early days, I would listen to people tell me it was not real, and that we were overreacting. Those pandemic deniers did not see the fear in my patients' eyes.

They did not have to watch hundreds of people die as many of my colleagues did. They did not have to come home fearful of making their loved ones sick.

At the time, I considered these people abusive and selfish. Now I see that they were just like me: afraid, searching for answers, and incapable of summoning the compassion we needed to see ourselves and each other through the biggest global crisis in our lifetimes. For many, our common humanity was hard to recognize in the early days of this pandemic, and it still eludes some of us.

As I look back at those days we spent as front-line workers at the beginning of the pandemic, I feel tremendous compassion and a sense of awe for who we were, what we did, and who we became. I also recall an utter lack of self-compassion, compassion for each other, and compassion for the state of our country and our world that made the crisis even more difficult and debilitating than it had to be. This lack of self-compassion and compassion remains with us today.

However, I am still hopeful.

Why I Wrote This Book

I have studied compassion for well over twenty years. The first time I realized I was not alone in this quest for more compassion was with Karen Armstrong, whose "Charter for Compassion" I signed in 2009. Studying compassion for me is also part rebellion; I grew up in a family where compassion was not at the forefront of our lives, and all of us are exposed to media (social and otherwise) that focuses far more on judgment than compassion.

At the time of this writing, I am completing my PhD with a dissertation on heart health, long-term stress measurements, self-compassion, compassion, and fear of compassion. I am a graduate of Stanford University's Applied Compassion Program in the Center for Compassion and Altruism Research and Education (CCARE). All these things together with my fierce and fiery infatuation with compassion inspired me to write this book. Researching and writing about compassion and the psychophysiology of it has brought me to a place where I believe compassion is accessible to all, even us—the burnt-out, overworked, hopeless, discouraged, and shocked who work in patient care every day.

Despite my long study, however, I have only recently begun to understand what compassion truly is (and just as importantly, what it *isn't*) and how we in this field both benefit from its presence and suffer when it is not in the forefront of our motivations and actions.

As professional caregivers and human beings, we need to address compassion at many levels where it's largely lacking. As a group, those of us in medicine are indoctrinated in a way you do not see in other professions. We are asked to be both caring and removed, to work long hours, and to do our work without error. We are expected to put aside the most basic of human needs like sleep, food, and personal breaks in order to help others. Not only is this not sustainable, but it is also abusive and the opposite of what we tell our patients to do to maintain their own health and well-being.

The looming question is this: how are we not as human as the rest?

There's also an underlying current of competition. I remember a day when, during an eight-hour shift, I treated thirty-eight patients in their cars on the roof of our building. I told a colleague how overwhelmed I felt. They replied, "Oh man, that sounds terrible. It's so busy. I saw forty-five the other day, and I was back first thing in the morning, doing it all over again."

This response was complicated, but it demonstrates how we are automatically trained to drive ourselves into the ground and are rewarded for doing so, and even compete for that sort of twisted recognition.

Now, I understand that there was an element of commiseration in that response, but the pride that person took in seeing forty-five patients disturbed me. I told them about my thirty-eight because it was so painful for me and I wanted it to stop. They mentioned their forty-five with a bit of glee and satisfaction in being able to do it. I began to wonder, "Did they connect with those patients? Did I connect with mine? Were we able to actually help any of them? Could this be the future of our medical care? Is this what we signed up for?"

I don't think it is.

The Remedy

My hope is that the research, analysis, and experiences I share in this book—which are drawn from more than twenty years of practicing medicine, and also from the sometimes messy and painful cultivation of my own compassionate practice—will help you move beyond the addiction to overwork that's endemic in the world of healthcare, and reconnect with why you first committed to this work. After three years of a global pandemic that has exposed so much dysfunction in our field, our hospitals, our patients, and ourselves, I hope this book will help us all take a step back from this broken system and often unhealthy caregiving culture, and reconsider what we demand of each other and of ourselves. Only then can we can work together to practice and live in a more sustainable way.

I also hope this book helps you reach a place of great self-compassion that radiates out, making the world not only a better place, but a place that we can be proud of.

Each chapter approaches a different aspect of pragmatic compassion—for others and for ourselves—drawing on evidence-based research and examples from my lived experience to explore the challenges and methods of developing compassionate practice, its psychophysiological underpinnings, the benefits of living and working with greater compassion, and the personal and professional costs of continuing to forge ahead without it.

With a greater knowledge of how to put compassion

into practice, I believe we will foster deep healing in our community. With the small changes suggested in this book we can, over time, make a significant difference in how we define, express, and appreciate compassion in our work and in our lives.

Compassion can transform all the care we give—to our patients, to ourselves, to our loved ones, and to our world.

Chapter One

DEFINING COMPASSION

"What do we live for if not to make the world less difficult for each other?"

– George Eliot (aka Mary Ann Evans)

COMPASSION. How do you define something so ethereal, and yet so grounded?

One of my favorite definitions is "to know no other." Well, what the hell does it mean to know no other? Does it mean that I'm sitting alone throughout my life, knowing that there's no "other" out there, only the dark abyss? No. What it means is that there truly *is* no other because we are all connected. What we experience, chances are, somebody else out there has experienced, too. It goes both ways.

If this is true, compassion, also defined as "to suffer with," makes perfect sense. We suffer together. When we break the word into its components, the first part, *com*, means "with." The second part of the word, *passion*, has many definitions: strong, enthusiastic emotions; an intense desire. When we look at the ontological origins of the word "passion," it comes from the Latin *pati*, which means suffering.

Suffering is simply this: wanting things to be different than they are.

I am 100 percent certain that you have had an experience of wanting a situation to be different than it is. I am certain I have had days or weeks at a time where this was true for me.

Compassion, for me personally, has always been a struggle—a struggle invisible to me, but a struggle all the same. As with many who practice medicine, my desire to help others began long before I obtained a medical license. Helping others and compassion go hand in hand. Unfortunately, helping others and pathology also have a correlation. For me, this second correlation was a strong one.

So many of us suffered traumas as children that paved the way for us to become healers and helpers. The traumatic events of my early life showed me clearly that I did not want anyone around me suffering, and if they were, I was certainly going to find a way to stop that suffering immediately.

In my eyes, personal suffering was a matter of life or death. At the age of ten, I found out that my "sister" was really my mother, and that my adoptive parents were really my grandmother and step-grandfather. At this time, I was sent to live with the woman I'd known as my sister because the man I'd called Dad (my step-grandfather) and the woman I'd called Ma (my grandmother) were getting divorced.

Ma took the divorce very hard. She tried several times to commit suicide. After one attempt when she nearly succeeded, the woman I knew as my sister felt it was time to let me know I was adopted. She thought Ma was going to die, and she wanted me to know I'd have one mother left if she did. Ma survived.

When I went back to the home I grew up in after Ma's last hospitalization, compassion, helping, and empathy became a big ol' ball of messy. At a very young age, I started figuring out how others felt as a survival mechanism and as a means to try to create safety and security for myself and those around me. As long as everyone else was happy and healthy, I could relax. As a child, I found it hard to differentiate their suffering from my own. This made it hard to tell which way the compassion should flow.

Also, times were different in the 1970s. Compassion was not in the parenting style book. In the '80s they called unskilled compassionate familial interactions "codependency," and some still do today. Of the many psychological boxes into which we try to put people and their complex feelings and relationships, I've always considered this one the most cruel. We pathologize people who have been victimized and vilify those who've been traumatized until we have a bunch of diagnoses and no healing. This leaves us so separated by our own labels and traumas that compassion has nowhere to grow.

But the seeds of compassion remain sewn into our DNA. Our lived experiences and common humanity create a rich and fertile soil.

Now, some of us have more manure in our gardens to help compassion grow. Most of the people I have worked with, and the most remarkable healers of our time, have suffered greatly—**many** of them much more than I. Maybe you, too, have suffered unimaginable losses and traumas that taught you great lessons in suffering and healing and called you into this field. That said, I do not believe one must suffer greatly to be skilled in compassion. I will say, though, that I have never met a great healer who has not suffered.

None of this comes automatically or easily. It took me years to grow into my understanding of what true compassion can do for those who are the helpers and those who are suffering (roles we will all choose or have thrust upon us at some point in our lives). Not everyone will have such a colorful story, but I know that we all have past experiences that shape our ability to forge the type of human connection and interaction that can truly save a life—or, at least, as Mary Ann Evans wrote under her *nom de plume* George Eliot in the quote that begins this chapter, enable us to make life less difficult for each other.

Even though this concept of "suffering with" or "being one with" each other seems relatively basic on the surface, we seem to have great difficulty pinning it down. Yet, we continue to try, and the extensive research done in this area can do much to help us understand.

The Five Qualities of Compassion

Throughout the medical and psychological communities, there is much debate about how to define compassion. In order to scientifically study a topic, you need to have a definition of what you are studying. This difficulty in defining the word "compassion" also makes compassion difficult to study.

It appears, however, that five qualities of compassion are gaining traction.

- **The first quality is awareness.** Awareness is the ability to recognize suffering.

- **The second quality is humility.** This quality connects us and gives us a greater capacity for compassion.

- **The third quality is embodiment.** This is having the capacity to tolerate uncomfortable feelings that arise and hold an openness and acceptance for the other person's suffering.

- **The fourth quality is common humanity.**
  Through this quality, we recognize that we all
  suffer, and that we all want to be happy, healthy,
  and safe.

- **The fifth quality is action,** which may be the
  most important. This is where we make a plan
  to act on our emotions to alleviate the other
  person's suffering.[1]

These five qualities are also the basis of the teachings
at the Center for Compassion and Altruism Research and
Education (CCARE) at Stanford University, a program
founded by James Doty, MD. If I were to add a sixth quality (or rule) of compassion, it would be that *compassion
is wise*. It does not create more suffering for anyone—
including the person offering compassion.

What Does Compassion Actually Look Like?

Imagine that you are treating a patient or seeing a friend
who has recently lost a loved one. The first quality of
compassion leads you to recognize that they are suffering.
You cannot help what you cannot see. The second quality,
humility, creates a greater capacity to help; we know we
are human, and witnessing a great (or small) suffering
is a great honor and should be held with reverence. The
third quality, embodiment, requires you to connect with

the distress and feel moved by it. At this point, you may remember what it felt like to lose somebody you loved. You might even recall what was comforting for you and how somebody showed compassion for you. Stay with it. Do not run away. This creates your capacity to be with the other person in their suffering. This may look different depending on who you are with.

Sitting with your patients or your loved ones in their suffering can be difficult. Having this capacity is a compassionate action in and of itself. This does not mean that you experience what they are experiencing, but that you are able to be present and attentive to their experience as they live through it. Some people call this "holding space." Others call it "being present." The sentinel quality of embodiment is not running away. Embodiment also helps you understand that suffering is absolutely normal, and in fact is a universal human experience. This leads us to the fourth quality, common humanity, which requires that we understand deeply that every human being wants to be free, safe, happy, and healthy, and wants this for their loved ones as well.

The fifth quality, action, is what distinguishes compassion from empathy and other feelings of connection. Feeling the motivation to alleviate the other person's suffering, and then taking action to do so, is the final quality that defines compassion.

Acting on the emotions you feel to lessen the other person's suffering is crucial. However, it is impossible to take away another person's suffering completely. Their suffering belongs to them, and they will know when to hold onto it and when to let it go. Striving to alleviate suffering, rather than eliminate it, is a more realistic goal. This is an important distinction. Being present can be the most rewarding hard work you do for someone who is suffering. Sit with them and breathe. Sit with them and cry. Offer them a hug. Just don't run away.

So, right here, right now, you can lay the burden down that you need to end all suffering. We are in this together, you are not alone. There are more of us than you know. Our voices will become louder, and our light will shine brighter so that we may find one another. I believe that sharing joy multiplies joy, and sharing sorrow diminishes sorrow. We may be able to diminish others' suffering simply by being there, and that is really beautiful if you think about it. It is also enough.

There are as many compassionate actions as there are stars in the galaxy. This can be a slippery slope and a tricky place for some people. I know I have often been caught in wanting so much to alleviate another's suffering that I caused myself to suffer. However, when you walk away in pain or exhaustion after having relieved someone else's suffering, this is not compassion.

We'll explore compassionate action (and how to provide compassion to others without letting it consume you) in detail later in this book.

COMPASSION AND EMPATHY

I have spent a significant amount of time contemplating

compassion, but even for me, compassion and empathy often get mixed up. I will discuss this more in Chapter Four, "Compassion and the Brain." However, I think it is important to introduce the distinction here.

Imagine you see a person drowning in the ocean. Without a doubt, you'll feel a certain amount of panic as you wonder what to do. Then you have some choices to make. In order to be helpful, your choice narrows down to two options: either jump in the water and try to rescue them or throw them a lifesaver.

When you jump in to save them, this is *not* compassion. This is empathy. Empathy is when you *feel* what the other person is feeling, which can diminish your ability to help them if you stay there too long. If you see someone drowning, sometimes jumping in might be the only way you can help them, but you should never do so without a life vest. In all scenarios, you are taking care of yourself first and bringing forth the power of compassion as your trusted guide. Once you've joined them in the water, without a life vest, you will feel wet, scared, and cold. You might even drown with them. There is another way.

If jumping in to save them is the empathetic response, throwing them a life preserver is the compassionate approach. You recognize the situation, and you recognize their feelings; you feel an empathetic response, but you do not stay in that empathetic space. You find an actionable way to help. You act to alleviate their suffering without causing additional suffering for yourself. This way is more likely to preserve both their life and your own. Now, *that* is compassion—both for self and for another.

Simply stated, the first rule of compassion is *do not jump in the water.* Jumping in is empathy. Empathy is not bad. It's just not as effective as compassion. As my mentor Neelama Eyres told me, "Empathy is like salt: a little makes things great; too much can be bad for your health."

More Theories of Compassion

I have encountered several other theories of compassion, each with its own merits. One holds that compassion consists of three facets: noticing, feeling, and responding to suffering.[2]

Another asserts that there are five attributes of compassion: care for well-being, sensitivity, empathy, distress tolerance, and common humanity.[3]

The Dalai Lama has spoken of the commitment to relieve the suffering of others while approaching it with an openness to the suffering that they are experiencing without judgment. The Dalai Lama has also made it very clear that there must be wisdom behind our compassionate actions. Don't drown in it.

Another way to define compassion is to examine "the three elements of compassion": kindness, common humanity, and mindfulness.[4]

The one thing that all these approaches have in common is that they all involve resonating with others' emotions or perceived emotions. I think this is where things can get confusing for many people.

How deeply we engage or identify with others' emotions is where the rubber meets the road. This is where we can go down a path of genuine compassion or get lost in other people's experiences, thereby inadvertently creating *more* suffering. We have all experienced that one patient whose suffering has pulled us down into the pit of their despair. For the rest of the day, and sometimes longer, our interactions with subsequent patients are less fulfilling and compassionate because we are stuck in that room with that first patient. Then, we bring the experience, and the associated emotions, home with us; this affects how we connect with our loved ones, and how much or little we are able to relax and reset. Sometimes, we're so wrapped up in the details of our patient's suffering that we carry it with us into sleep (or lack thereof).

This is not compassion. It is an unhealthy attachment pattern that will ultimately deplete us to the point where compassion is no longer accessible. So, how can we counteract this tendency to carry other people's burdens?

We do it through *action.*

Compassion, in my opinion, must incorporate action in order to be complete. I often say, "Compassion is a noun that acts like a verb." It's something we are, and it's also something we do.

It is imperative to understand that being present—for yourself or someone else—is an *action*. Being still and listening is an *action*. Allowing space and time for someone's suffering is an *action*.

"Allow" is a verb. "Allowing," in the context of compassion, means "to give the necessary time or opportunity for something to arise, to heal, or to die."

When my Ma passed (luckily, several years after her divorce and the events I described above), I was able to allow her a compassionate death. The day before she died, she said to me, "I think I'm dying, and I'm scared."

I panicked inside, but I knew I did not want to add to her suffering during this precious time. So, I told her, "I am here, I will hold your hand until you get to wherever you are going, I am fierce and will not let go until you feel safe. When you are ready, you let go of my hand, deal?"

She smiled and said, "I love you the most."

She died in my home, and in my arms, shortly after this conversation. I did nothing to change the situation. There are things you cannot change. It was painful for me to let her go, but it was not painful for me to give her the grace of a good death, and a safe place to die.

I did not die with her. I could never fully take her suffering away. We both wanted things to be different than they were, and we were both suffering. But my compassionate action did not *create* my pain—that came from the loss of her, the wanting for her to continue to live. My compassionate action was allowing the process to unfold without my intervention. Fighting it, trying to stop or delay it, would have created more pain. In situations like this, *nothing to be done* gets everything done.

If you suffer greatly through your version of compassionate action, I can assure you that what you are doing is not compassion. So please, as you examine your personal definitions of and relationship to compassion, remember this: *The suffering you witness does not have to become suffering you experience in order for you to provide a place of solace and peace for those suffering.*

Chapter Two

EXPLORING SELF-COMPASSION

*"If your compassion does not include yourself,
it is incomplete."*

– **Buddha**

HOW WE RELATE to ourselves, and the degree to which we give ourselves compassion, can affect every aspect of how we relate to and have compassion for others.

We are all hard on ourselves to some degree. Whether it's something as insignificant as missing a deadline, or something more powerful like letting a loved one down when they needed us the most, we know what it feels like to blame and shame ourselves. Sometimes, we beat ourselves up for things we didn't do, or things we witnessed but had little to no control over; in fact, I'd argue that, within the medical community, these last two are the things over which we beat ourselves up the most.

As medical professionals, we are expected to show compassion to others. Yet, we are pros at berating ourselves. There are so many opportunities for us to shine, and many more moments where the pressures and realities of our jobs can bring us to our knees.

I was about three years into practicing emergency medicine when I was named in a lawsuit. I was the first person to see the patient who filed the suit, but certainly not the last. We were all sued.

The case followed me for ten years. Each time I had to be re-credentialed for the hospital, I had to put down all the details yet again. Even though the case was eventually dismissed with prejudice, that didn't help me at all. Before that I endured two or three years of sheer torture. The things that plaintiffs will say about you in a lawsuit are horrific. I was called reckless, negligent, and incompetent. It was assumed that whatever I did that caused someone harm, I did out of either stupidity or malicious intent.

Perhaps the hardest part is that you cannot talk to anyone but your lawyer about the case. You cannot ask other professionals if they have been sued, what they did, or how they coped. It is a legal nightmare as well as a personal one—and it provides a prime opportunity for us to beat ourselves up in a shameful, secretive, and also very public way. When we are sued for medical malpractice, we are guilty until proven innocent.

All of the things that we fear about not being good enough, not knowing enough, not being careful enough; all those nights of lost sleep thinking of the patients we could have done more for, or the cases where we could have missed something; all of these self-doubts that pile up unaddressed over the years—these hit you right in the gut when you see it all in writing. I remember being coached by the hospital's attorneys when I was being deposed. All I wanted to do was to tell the plaintiff I was sorry he had had such a bad experience and a bad outcome. But apologizing is forbidden. Apologizing means admitting you've done something wrong. Apologizing means you'll lose the case, your insurance rates will go up, and the hospital won't be happy. I learned how to answer questions with one or two words, or the phrase "I do not recall" if I did not have a crystal-clear recollection of what happened on the day I saw that patient. (Full disclosure here: I *don't* have a crystal-clear memory of what I ate for breakfast this morning, so I said "I do not recall" quite a bit.)

And then, of course, there are the patients who don't sue us, but who have bad outcomes that can't be avoided. We can do everything right and things still go wrong. In a strange way, those might be the hardest to forgive ourselves for.

It's hard to explain to people who don't practice medicine the degree of responsibility, and the corresponding degree of self-flagellation, that can occur when we make the simplest of mistakes. You click the wrong box in an EHR, and the next thing you know the patient is getting the wrong dose of medication or the wrong medication altogether. You miss asking that one critical question that would lead you to a diagnosis that has stumped you for years. Or you just get a patient with so many complaints that it's overwhelming even for you, and you feel this combination of just being over it—and, simultaneously, guilt for feeling "over it"—which catapults you into a not-so-good place.

All the while, we try to hold each other up by saying, "It's okay, we're human. Everybody makes mistakes." But in medicine, the stakes are literally life and death. By not acknowledging that, we do a disservice to ourselves and the patients we serve. We need compassion—and furthermore, we need *self-compassion*—more than just about any other group of professionals on the planet.

All this pressure can build up over time. We can only work so many hours in a day, so many days in a week, so many weeks in a month, and so many months in a year before we are exhausted—and, when we are exhausted, we're more likely to make these mistakes. However, due to expectations and our own sense of responsibility, we are completely off-base in how little time we actually take to rest and care for ourselves. I don't know what the ratio is for you, but for me, after I work two days in a row, I need two days off to recover. Thankfully, I'm at the point in my career where that's possible, but I couldn't always take that time in the early days.

In fact, I didn't learn the necessity of self-compassion until 2015, when I became the primary caretaker for my maternal grandmother (Ma), who had suffered a stroke and needed twenty-four-hour care. I was still working. I had a young child, and my husband was working long hours as he built his career as an attorney. I cannot tell you how exhausted I became.

Then, Ma began to get out of bed and wander at night. Losing precious sleep was the last straw for my own capacity. Finally, I decided to use a Board and Care facility so that she had a safe place to sleep. Leaving her there was the hardest thing I have ever done in my life, but it was necessary for me. I would pick her up every morning and she would spend the day at my house unless there was a relative scheduled to visit her at the facility. (The relatives came maybe twice a year, if that.)

She was in my home when we had the conversation I shared in Chapter One; she died in my arms, in her mobile hospital bed, in the safe space I had created. I'm glad I was able to give her a good death, and the truth—that doing so from a place of exhaustion and depletion was also one of the hardest things I've ever done—does not negate the experience.

If you have ever taken care of a loved one at the end of their life, you know that any moment you're away from them feels like torture—just like every minute that you're with them. For me, there seemed to be no escape from the self-blame and wishing I could do more. I know part of this is just me being human. However, I also know that part of this is built on my medical training: you show up, do the job, suck it up, and keep moving forward—and think about yourself later, if at all.

However, after decades of putting everyone else first, this was the last straw. I was drained to the point where I had no compassion left—not for my patients, not for my family, not for my grandmother, and certainly not for myself. My body gave out.

What I learned during that period was that no one could take better care of me than me. And until I did that, I had no business taking care of other people.

I know that can be a little rough for some people to swallow because, both as humans and as medical professionals, we're trained to care for others at the expense of our own well-being. Many of us have childhood traumas that created situations and behavioral patterns of saving the day and people-pleasing to the degree where this seems almost normal. However, it is now time for compassion to find its place within us, both for ourselves and for others.

The pervasive self-blame and self-punishment I saw in myself, and still see in my colleagues, rivals any traumatic event I've ever seen. What does this do to our minds, our bodies, and our spirits? Is there a way to transform this personal self-flagellation into something beautiful and healing? Is there a gentler, kinder way of relating to ourselves that could create an internal environment for health and healing?

The answer is yes. And the remedy is compassion.

The Five Myths of Self-Compassion

When I'm trying to find out what something is, I tend to look at what it is not. This helps me wrap my head around concepts with more ease.

I also look to the experts. Kristin Neff, PhD, is an expert in the field of self-compassion. I find her "Five Myths of Self-Compassion" very helpful in describing what compassion is not, and thus revealing what compassion is.

Myth 1: Compassion is Self-Pity

The first myth Dr. Neff discusses is the idea that self-compassion is self-pity. Self-pity is more a state of feeling sorry for oneself, wondering why things are so bad or what we did to deserve such a terrible outcome. Wallowing in the negativity of a situation disconnects us from our true selves and our interconnectedness with other people. The separation from others is a hallmark quality of self-pity.

Now, before we get all highfalutin and think, "I have *never* done that!" let's take a step back.

We have *all* done this at one point or another in our lives. Feeling sorry for ourselves and our plight has been romanticized in our culture. It's a lot more dramatic and exciting to hear a story with victims and villains than to listen to the truth of the human condition and how it is difficult for all of us.

The concept of *common humanity* is one of the three elements of compassion introduced in Chapter One. What this means is that all of us, as human beings, essentially want the same things. We want to be happy, healthy, and successful, and to live a long and prosperous life. We all want our loved ones to have the same, and to be protected from the things we deem unfair, cruel, or harmful.

Every. Single. One of us.

Now, what makes us happy, what we perceive as unfair or harmful, and who we identify as family may differ from person to person. One person's family may be very traditional—mom, dad, brothers, sisters, aunts, uncles, etc. Another's family may be fellow gang members. We also stand up and protect and care for each other in very different ways outwardly, but the underlying sentiment is the same. Pema Chödrön, the United States' first Buddhist nun, says it best: "Everyone loves something, even if it is just tortillas."

We, as a collective, are in desperate need of remembering our common humanity. Believe it or not, we're all in this life together. Ours is a shared human experience, and we need to start getting along. Recognizing our common humanity is a pillar of compassion.

Pain and suffering happen to all of us. These things happen—not because we did something right or wrong, good, or bad, but because we are human. Ironically, this is an excellent place for compassion to start.

Those who practice self-compassion regularly are less likely to end up adrift in the sea of self-pity. In our struggles and difficulties lay the potential for remarkable transformation and healing. We've got to be able to sit with what really is happening in order to create space for healing.

Myth 2: Self-Compassion is Weak

The second myth Dr. Neff discusses is the notion that self-compassion is weak. I can think of nothing more vital and fierce than to see a person who has failed miserably stand up, dust themselves off, and try again. It doesn't mean that things are not rough, complex, or painful. There is an inherent gentleness in true strength. The kind of strength that we need to be fully human does not reside in physical strength or mental hardness. It resides in cognitive flexibility and our ability to see our struggles and joys in a realistic way that enables us to fully live in the experience of being human. The reality is, practicing self-compassion actually increases resiliency and strength. Self-compassion increases our ability to cope with difficulties as they occur throughout our lives. This sounds like anything but weakness to me.

Throughout my years of practicing medicine, I have witnessed so much bravery coupled with vulnerability that, if you were there to see what I saw, you would weep uncontrollably. I am sure that you, too, have witnessed and personally experienced many moments that have tested, stretched, and strengthened your capacity for compassion.

Please, if you remember anything from this book, remember this: *You are* a compassionate badass. You may just not know it yet.

Many years ago, shortly before I completed my medical training, I was doing my emergency department rotation. Most of what I treated was fairly benign—a couple of broken bones here, some lacerations there. But every once in a while, something heartbreaking would come through the door.

One night I saw a young boy who had drowned in one of the rivers in the surrounding area. When he arrived by ambulance, they had CPR in progress and we took over the CPR. His parents rushed in behind us. You could see the frantic fear in both of their eyes as well as their helplessness. We all knew that the child was gone, but we were doing the CPR compassionately. We were doing it for the parents so that they could see that we were doing everything we possibly could to save their child. We had IVs and medications flowing. One of our physicians was on the gurney doing compressions and there I was, standing at the head of the bed, bagging breath into this child, watching his chest rise and fall—and knowing that he wasn't breathing at all.

I don't know exactly how long we performed CPR, but it felt like hours. I distinctly remember meeting the eyes of my colleagues. All of us wanted to stop so badly because we knew it was over. The sound of his ribs breaking and cracking was torture, but we also knew we couldn't stop just yet. The mom and dad were still watching hopefully.

Finally, my attending physician called the code, the time of death noted. Then he said, "It's your turn, Catherine." I knew exactly what he meant: I was tasked with telling the parents that their preteen child was gone.

This was my first time telling parents that their child had died, and it was one of the hardest days of my entire life.

Calmly, I walked up to the parents. They knew what I was going to say. But they didn't start crying until I said, "I'm sorry, we did everything we could do." They fell into each other's arms, and I stood there holding all the space around them, wishing I could take their pain away but knowing that I couldn't.

The compassion that I felt for these parents is still with me today. The compassion I feel for myself—for the fear I felt around telling them, the discomfort I felt in their vulnerability, and the exquisitely intense emotions of that moment—will never leave me. I have compassion for myself when I feel the ache of knowing that their child would be in his thirties by now. He might have had a family himself. I often imagine that there's a parallel universe where this young man grew up happy and hopeful, bringing the world special gifts that only he could bring. I see his parents happy, knowing that their son was safe.

For my magical thinking, I have a ton of self-compassion, as I know it saves my heart from shattering on some days.

Whatever our training taught us, it is inhumane to not be present and human—both for others and for ourselves. There are healthy boundaries, and then there is cold detachment. Allowing tears to fall is different than wailing along with the bereaved. Allowing our emotions to be seen is healing to our patients. It does not take away from the patient; in fact, it validates the awful nature of their experience. And it does not take away from our expertise and authority; rather, it makes us infinitely more trustworthy.

This type of compassionate care may be extreme by some standards, but it is also complete, 100-percent-badass-warrior compassion energy, and it's necessary in a world where children die every day without cause or need. True compassion isn't for the weak of heart. True compassion shows up in the way that it can, while it can, when it can, for as long as it can, without harming the vessel that delivers it.

Remember that. When compassion hurts you, or weakens you, it is *no longer compassion.*

Myth 3: Self-Compassion Causes Complacency

Dr. Neff's third myth of compassion is that it can make us complacent. Too much compassion for ourselves, we reason, will compromise our "no pain, no gain" mentality and prevent us from thriving and moving forward. If we're not criticizing ourselves and feeling bad about ourselves, what will happen to our motivation to improve?

None of us like it when we fail, make missteps, or behave in ways we aren't proud of. But if these things are *not* happening in our lives, we are not living the entire human experience. It's part of the deal.

In 2012, a research project demonstrated that, when a group of participants practiced self-compassion concerning an event that they historically felt guilty for, this quality strengthened their accountability and motivation to do better in the future.[1] Taking ourselves out of the fires of guilt and shame allows us to see ourselves as humans having a shared experience with other human beings. Through self-compassion, we can reach a place of grace for ourselves, and do better in the bargain.

Myth 4: Self-Compassion is Narcissism

Narcissism is getting a lot of press these days. Newsflash: As fully alive human beings, we all possess some narcissistic qualities. This does not mean that we all suffer from narcissism. In fact, the condition is actually quite rare, with only 0–5.3 percent of the general population having this disorder.[2] Therefore, Dr. Neff's fourth myth is quite an easy one to disprove.

That said, it's important to understand how self-compassion differs from self-esteem. Self-esteem is thinking of oneself as good or even better than others and can be a slippery slope indeed. Self-esteem can rise and fall depending on if we perceive ourselves as successful or unsuccessful in any given task or life event. This way of viewing ourselves is inherently fragile. In a more narcissistic, self-esteem-driven way of thinking, we need to feel superior to others, and when we aren't feeling superior to others, we're thinking less of ourselves. This is exhausting: so much work for so little connection to ourselves or others.

Self-compassion, on the other hand, requires us to befriend the imperfections that we all possess. Even when we are in our most humiliating states of being, when we do wrong, when we make mistakes big or small, self-compassion is right there waiting for us with a strength that allows us to experience what it is like to be fully human.

Myth 5: Self-Compassion is Selfish

Dr. Neff's fifth myth of self-compassion is that it is selfish. Women struggle with this aspect of self-compassion more than their male counterparts.[3] This may seem counterintuitive, as we tend to attribute compassion and care to the feminine more than the masculine.

Compassion is strong and vital. Strength and vitality do not know (or care) what sex you are. However, society is not always so discerning.

Historically, women have been conditioned to believe that focusing on themselves is selfish. It is not a significant leap to understand that the concept of self-compassion may be more difficult for women than men. However, it is interesting that our ability to be nurturing and kind to each other expands when we are nurturing and kind to ourselves. This does not mean pedicures, champagne brunches, and long days of Netflix binge-watching in our PJs. (Although these things are not inherently wrong, they are *not* self-compassion.) Self-compassion means showing up for ourselves in a way that we would show up for our closest friends and loved ones when they are in the pit with the wolves circling their tender hearts.

When most of us tend to beat ourselves up first, overcoming this tendency may take some time and practice. Beating ourselves up, Neff warns us, can be a paradoxical form of self-centeredness. The self-flagellation can draw all of our attention to the self, rendering us unable to see our humanity and interconnections with others and our fundamental goodness. When we can meet our own emotional needs with self-compassion, we have more bandwidth to share our nurturing, loving-kindness with others. How fantastic is that?

Self-Compassion Belongs in Medicine

We've defined what self-compassion is not. Now, we have a better idea of what it is.

Simply put, self-compassion gives our struggles a solid, grounded place to land, knowing we are not alone in the labors of life. It allows us to be nurtured and to connect with ourselves, giving us the strength to connect more deeply with others and move forward with compassion for all.

More, as you're about to learn in upcoming chapters, both self-compassion and compassion for others have measurable positive effects within our bodies. Compassion reduces stress, can help lower blood sugar levels, and benefits our hearts and brains. It can even reduce cancer risks.

So, what would it look like if we put self-compassion into practice in the medical field?

It might look different for different people, but for me it's this: When I need to take time off, I do. When I need to slow down and see fewer patients, I do. Now, I know some people would argue, "If I don't see them, who will?" I promise you, somebody will, or the patients will find somewhere else to go. That's okay. We do not have to save every single person in the waiting room. Without our being there, the world will not stop. Instead, somebody who *does* have the energy to help will step up, and it will be fine.

We've been led to believe that we are the only ones that can do what we do, when and how we're doing it. However, this isn't true. It's okay to slow down, breathe, and let someone else step up. This is self-compassion.

My work life changed when I finally found compassion for what I had been through. At work, my self-compassion increased to the degree that I felt ready to share my insights with others, and it started to help them too. Today, when I need time off, I take it. Vacation-shaming is over for me! Now, when I feel exhausted, I work slower, or not at all. The patients wait longer to see me, but they get a better version of me when they do. I am not saying every patient encounter is perfect, but they sure are better than they were two years ago.

I won't lie, I still have bad days when I wonder why I do what I do. But then I get that one patient—you know, the one who truly appreciates you and benefits from seeing you—and I come back to my center.

We cannot control the whole world, and going faster does not mean doing better. Self-compassion helps you *and* the patients. It keeps us all safe. Powering through is not in the best interest of the patients. Our patients need us rested, focused, and healed, not stressed, frustrated, and overwhelmed. When we're not at our best, we make mistakes—and the shame and guilt of those mistakes beat us down even more.

Also, I will say this: If there is not enough staff to see the patients, then the problem is not you. The problem is the system and its greed. (Don't believe me? Just look up how much your CEOs make). This isn't just a moral problem; it's a safety problem. We need to feel safe to practice, to have the support and space to do our job of helping patients heal. If your system does not support your self-care, *leave*. If enough of us were to do this, we could change the face of medicine in the most healing way. Compassion both for self and others is the revolution of a new day.

Chapter Three

COMPASSION AND THE HEART

"A hard heart makes for hard judgments;
a compassionate heart understands the humanity
of the one we presume to judge."

– Joan Chittister

WHEN DISCUSSING COMPASSION, we often conjure images of a heartfelt experience. We might mention the heart—not in a physiological way, but in a romanticized way that alludes to a loving, warm feeling. However, there is more to the heart and compassion than simple romance and wishful thought.

The connection between compassion and the heart is more than metaphorical. Compassion specifically affects the physiology of the cardiovascular system.

My first experience with the effect of lack of compassion on the heart occurred on an autumn day when I was running through midtown Sacramento. It was a gorgeous day: the perfect temperature, with little white fluffy clouds in the sky and a canopy of trees shading the streets. My favorite running partner—my golden retriever, Sundance—was running alongside me.

My biological mother (the woman I had grown up thinking of as my sister) had recently passed away, and I was using running (and wine) to cope with my grief. I kept telling myself that everything would be okay. I just need to power through and get over my mother's dying.

As I was running, I started to feel tension in my chest that turned into pain.

At that point in my life, chest pain was a sign that I should pick up the pace and run through it, but as I ran faster, the pain got worse. I started to slow down. I got dizzy, and held onto a stop sign to keep myself upright. (Pretty ironic scene, really.) I was concerned, but I figured I could wait it out until I felt better and then walk home.

When I got home, the pain continued, so I decided it might be a good idea to get it checked out. I was an otherwise healthy thirty-four-year-old with no significant medical issues to date. I went to the emergency department and got my heart checked out. They drew the right labs, they did the right tests, and everything looked normal.

I went home somewhat confused, wondering what was going on with me. Honestly, they don't teach you how to make sense of this kind of thing when you're learning to practice medicine. They don't show you in any meaningful way how much emotions, grief, or lack of compassion for yourself can affect your health. They tell us that anxiety can create a lot of lookalike illnesses and maladies, but they don't emphasize with the appropriate amount of importance the psychophysiological ramifications of not being kind to yourself.

It took me many years to really start to understand this for myself. After that day, I suffered from heart palpitations that were relentless. I had runs of supraventricular tachycardia (SVT) that made me feel as though I were actually dying. I had many visits to emergency departments thinking, *This is it. This is the time. This is the big one, I'm going down.* The whole time, I was very hard on myself, wondering why I couldn't be healthy and vibrant like before. I beat myself up for not being able to do everything the way that I used to be able to do it. Then, there was the self-punishment of wasting the time of other medical professionals if nothing was wrong. There was no self-compassion for the loss I just suffered and the increasing responsibilities that loss created.

This inner turmoil snowballed into a complicated medical conversation every single time I went to see a physician. Whenever they would tell me nothing was wrong, every cell in my body would scream, "Oh, but there is! Something is *very* wrong!" It was not a calling of my body to heal, but rather the calling of my spirit and *heart* to the elusive melody of compassion.

What "Heartfelt Experience" Really Means

No one could pinpoint the problem with my heart because my condition didn't have a clear physiological origin. Instead, it had psychological/emotional/spiritual origins that affected my physiology. It was not "histrionics." It was not merely anxiety. The anxiety was a symptom of something more. The chest pain and heart palpitations were a sign that *my heart was broken.*

You cannot discuss broken hearts without mentioning Takotsubo cardiomyopathy or Takotsubo syndrome (TTS). The name originates from the Japanese *takotsubo*, which means "octopus trap," as the heart takes on the shape of this device. TTS is a known heart disorder that occurs when we experience significant heartbreak or emotion in our lives. I was not diagnosed with this syndrome; however, it is one dramatic example of how our cardiovascular well-being is tied to our emotional well-being.

There was truly only one cure for my broken heart, and it began with the awareness that I had been terribly harsh with myself. My autonomic nervous system was in high gear. After I reached that awareness and recognized what I was doing to myself, I grieved. I grieved for the parts of myself that I left alone to deal with the harshness of being human. In that grief, I started to find little bits of light shining through the cracks of my broken heart; over many years, these began to illuminate my lack of self-compassion.

It took many events, gains, and losses before I was able to feel self-compassion. It took time, and it still takes effort, to be gentle with and kind to myself when things don't go according to my wishes and desires, and my relationship with self-compassion is still evolving today.

Compassion only became part of my daily life when I had no other place to go. It wasn't like I joyfully laid down my struggle and said, "Today, I am going to start being compassionate with myself and others." I spent *years* in a wrestling match with compassion until self-compassion finally pinned me to the floor and said, "How about now?" And even then, I was only capable of leaning into the pain of my broken heart.

Still, it was a first step. My heart was now leading the way.

It was so difficult for me to give up the relentless chatter in my brain—the voice that kept telling me that if I could achieve more, be more effective, or just build a time machine, everything would finally be okay. I just needed to pick more things up and run faster! However, what I truly needed was to learn to put more things down. I needed to put down my self-judgment, self-loathing, and self-criticism, and start picking up the pieces of myself that were crushed all around me.

As I started to pick up these pieces, one by one, I understood the reason why my heart couldn't beat steady and strong at this point in my life. For years I had been living in my head, convinced that that was the way to keep myself safe from harm. But harm came anyway.

Harm came, and it broke my heart in the way it does for each of us.

I can guarantee you that at some point in your life, harm will come to you and break your heart as well. However, with the knowledge that we are all in this together and none of us will get out of here alive or unscathed, we might just find a way to cover ourselves and each other with a good, soft blanket of compassion. If we can do that, we just might be able to heal.

My heart was the first part of my body to let me know something was wrong. So now, when I'm struggling, my heart is the first part of my body to which I ask the question, "What can I do for you?" My heart is where I begin. I find that when I start with my heart, the rest of my body aligns with its perfect, precious rhythm. This may be the perfect place for you to start, too.

Measuring Compassion's Impact on Cardiovascular Health

We are only beginning to understand the relationship between levels of compassion and the health of the human heart and cardiovascular system. When evaluating compassion's effect on the heart and cardiac system, two measures show promise: blood pressure and heart rate variability (HRV). Blood pressure and HRV have two overlapping mechanisms of control: the autonomic nervous system (sympathetic and parasympathetic branches) and baroreceptors.

The largest study to date on blood pressure and compassion showed that people who scored higher on compassion questionnaires had lower diastolic and systolic blood pressure levels as adults.[1] The researchers used data from The Young Finns study with over a thousand participants, showing that not only were the blood pressure measurements within normal limits, but these individuals also had a decreased risk of developing hypertension over a lifetime.

Carotid artery wall thickness appears to be affected as well, which can have a direct effect on blood pressure. A 2021 study discovered that women in midlife with higher levels of self-compassion had lower levels of subclinical cardiovascular disease as measured by carotid wall thickness.[2]

Blood pressure is easy to measure; however, the pathophysiological mechanisms underpinning hypertension are not simple by any stretch of the imagination. Control of blood pressure in the body is a complex mechanism driven by many body systems. Often there is a genetic predisposition to hypertension; however, multiple other factors are also at play.

The following is a very basic reminder of the complexity of the systems that control blood pressure.

- **Baroreceptors** help control blood pressure by sensing the stretch of the vessels coming from your heart out to the body (aorta) and your neck going up to the brain (carotid).

- **The renin-angiotensin-aldosterone system** helps with fluid and salt balance.

- **Endothelium of the vessels.** Endothelial cells release substances that control vasodilation and constriction.

- **Nitric oxide and endothelin-1** contribute to the regulation and maintenance of vascular tone and dilation.

As you read this, consider how magnificent it is that compassion can have an effect on blood pressure by influencing these vital regulatory systems. The best way to understand this is to look at the overlapping mechanism of the autonomic nervous system and the baroreceptors in more detail.

The sympathetic branch of our autonomic nervous system, when activated, causes catecholamines to be released. These substances increase renal (kidneys) activity, increasing sodium retention and increasing your blood pressure. We do not want our blood pressure to be too high or too low, so balance here is critical.

Baroreceptors pick up on the pressure in the vessel and send signals to dilate blood vessels (lowering blood pressure) or constrict blood vessels (elevating blood pressure). These two systems work with many other regulatory systems to ensure our blood pressure is right and keep us alive and healthy. This baroreceptor mechanism also affects our heart rate and is the driver of respiratory sinus arrhythmia associated with HRV (more on that shortly).

We are also looking for a balance of the parasym-pathetic and sympathetic branches of the autonomic nervous system. When they are out of balance, our HRV dips. Lower levels of HRV are associated with poor cardiac health.

WHY HRV MATTERS

HRV is a hot topic in medicine right now. But what exactly is heart rate variability, and what is its relation-ship to compassion?

The simplest definition is the time between each heart-beat and how it changes. Why would this be important? It's important because you want your heart to be able to respond to what's happening in your environment. When you run, you want your heartbeat to speed up to deliver blood and oxygen to your muscles and brain. When you're sitting on the couch binge-watching your favorite Netflix series and scarfing popcorn, you want your heart to slow down to conserve energy and create a resting state.

Once we know that the heart rate changes upon the body's demand, the next question is: *how* does it do this? The following is a very simplified description of heart rate variability.

First, understand that both short-term and long-term regulatory mechanisms control this beat-to-beat interval. Among the short-term regulatory mechanisms are baro-receptors. Again, these receptors are located in your aorta and your carotids. When you inhale, baroreceptors detect the rising pressure, and your heart will beat more rapidly. When you exhale, blood pressure falls, the baroreceptors sense that, and your heart rate decreases. This cycle repeats throughout the day. In medical terminology, this process is called *respiratory sinus arrhythmia* (RSA). Do not let the word arrythmia fool you: *arrhythmia* simply means a change (irregularity) in the heartbeat rhythm. Irregular doesn't necessarily equal abnormal; in the case of RSA, it is actually a sign of cardiac responsiveness and health.

There are two types of measurements for HRV: time domain and frequency domain. Applying *time-domain* measurements to HRV makes sense because we're trying to figure out the time interval between heartbeats. One of the most common research measurements utilized historically is the standard deviation of the inter-beat intervals of normal sinus beats (SDNN). This is the time between each beat, and also the differences between each beat compared to each other. In this measurement, premature ventricular beats (PVCs) or skipped beats have been removed. When those beats are not removed, it's called a standard deviation of the inter-beat intervals for all sinus beats (SDRR). Root mean square of successive RR interval differences (RMSSD) is currently gaining more popularity as the measure used in research today because it gives us the most accurate information on vagally (parasympathetic) mediated changes in HRV. It is less affected by respirations than RSA and is also associated with high-frequency power (also a parasympathetic dominant measurement). We will discuss the vagus nerve and the parasympathetic nervous system in depth in Chapter Five.

There are also *frequency-domain* measurements of HRV. This type of measurement requires transformation from raw data into its parts, which can be accomplished in a few different ways. Typically, scientists are most familiar with the use of a Fast Fourier Transformer (FFT) that takes the raw data (the heart signal) and separates the data into the corresponding frequencies. We measure the frequency in hertz (Hz). In medicine, the most typical place to see FFT is with EKG/EEG measurements.

A low frequency (LF) band is measured from 0.04 Hz to 0.15 Hz. Baroreceptor activity is most easily detected from this band.

A high-frequency band that ranges from 0.15 Hz to 0.40 Hz typically represents parasympathetic activity. This band has also been called the "respiratory band" because of its association with respiratory sinus arrhythmia. Low levels of this frequency are associated with stress and anxiety.

You may come across the term *LF/HF Ratio* in your own investigation of HRV. Some claim that this ratio gives you a balance between the sympathetic and parasympathetic nervous systems. This statement is not based on solid scientific research, nor does it provide an appreciation of the complexity and confounders that create heart rate variability.

WHAT THE RESEARCH SAYS

Let's look at more of the research on compassion and the cardiovascular system, particularly HRV.

The Center for Compassion and Altruism Research and Education at Stanford University published an article to evaluate the current trend in HRV training and compassion. Specifically, the article focused on training compassion to increase heart rate variability and, conversely, training heart rate variability to increase compassion.[3] This demonstrates the importance of self-regulation as an important component of compassion. The researchers noted that there have been several studies demonstrating that lower heart rate variability is present in conditions such as depression, anxiety, and self-criticism, and there are links between compassion and heart rate variability.[4] Research also notes that the impact of compassion on our physiology has been observed in our cardiovascular system. We understand that compassion helps alleviate suffering and, in some cases, prevents it altogether.

Compassion is challenging to measure quantitatively, but HRV offers a measurement that expresses the effects of compassion on our heart health quantitatively. Considering that cardiovascular disease is the number one cause of death for humans, I believe this is well worth investigating.

In 2016, researchers found that higher levels of self-compassion increased levels of HRV and noted that those with lower levels of self-compassion had heightened levels of anxiety. This may correlate to an increased ability to psychologically adapt to stress—again, showing the links between self-regulation, HRV, and compassion.[5]

Arch et al showed that compassionate imagery (imagining compassion coming from another source, either human or non-human) showed mixed results. Some of the participants had a decrease in HRV. Those who had that decrease also displayed much lower feelings of safety in social situations. These subjects also had high levels of self-criticism and experienced an anxious attachment as children.[6] The important thing to see here is that compassion directly affects the heart.

I find it particularly interesting that HRV may help us uncover unacknowledged trauma and other psychopathologies that affect our human experience and our health both physically and psychologically. Knowing that HRV is lower in those who have suffered early childhood adverse events, coupled with the fact that compassion has a measurable effect on HRV, we may have another avenue of healing to add to the current lexicon.

It appears that self-compassion training can change a woman's response to social threat when measured by cardiac function during the perceived threat, and our recovery from this perceived threat.[7] Unfortunately, in the world we live in, there is no clearly defined way to increase safety and decrease the feelings of threat for women. However, knowing that there are things that we can do to help our bodies recover from these insults and aggressions gives us power and control of our own well-being in the long term.

Physiological responses when studied with men show similar results.[8] This study demonstrated that men trained in self-compassion had higher vagally mediated heart rate variability. In addition, they showed an increase in heart rate variability when a stressor was presented to them—a time when one would expect to see a decrease. This shows that an increase in heart rate variability may benefit us not only in the recovery of a stressful event but during that stressful event as well.

Increased heart rate variability with self-compassion and compassion training is also linked with lower physical pain.[9] This study used a cold pain protocol to see if pain thresholds increased, or if the feeling of and response to pain lowered. They found that cold pain threshold responses were higher in those who received compassion training with higher HRV.

MIRROR WORK

I've always been a fan of motivational author Louise Hay. I was fortunate enough to meet her in 2009 at a conference in San Jose. I talked to her, hugged her, and asked her to sign a card. She wrote the most fantastic thing on the card: "Joy Heals, Love Louise."

Louise was always ahead of the curve. I have referenced her book *You Can Heal Your Life* for many years. One of her central beliefs and teachings is a practice she calls *mirror work,* in which you look in the mirror and say lovely things to yourself. Sounds simple enough, right? Her belief is that doing this daily can heal many physical and psychological ills. She was also convinced that the heart and the brain were connected by way of emotions.

It's a nice thought, but does it really work? Look at these two pieces of research and decide for yourself.

First, a group in Rome, Italy, studied compassion at the mirror. Their study tested whether self-compassion in front of the mirror would increase heart rate variability. They asked eighty-six participants to say four compassion-based phrases that they would use with a best friend to encourage and soothe them. The researchers separated the subjects into three groups. One group would repeat the four phrases to themselves without the mirror, a second group would say the compassionate phrase while looking in a mirror, and the third group would look at themselves in the mirror without repeating any phrase.

The study showed that the mirror work did, in fact, increase the efficacy of self-compassion, and also increased heart rate variability.[10]

The second study showed how the effects of compassion on the heart are also connected to the brain. In a study done in 2009, it was found that the blood oxygen level-dependent (BOLD) signal in the right middle insula showed a significant association with the heart. When compassion training occurred, this association grew stronger than in those who were not trained in compassion meditation. Data revealed a coupling of heart rate variability and the BOLD signal in the compassionate state compared to a neutral state in the dorsal anterior cingulate cortex.[11]

There are neurological cells in the heart, and they are connected with the brain.

Sadly, Louise Hay passed away in August 2017. I sincerely wish that she could have seen the mirror research before her passing. However, I feel that Louise did not need this research to validate what she knew to be true in her lifetime.

WHEREVER YOU ARE, START THERE

What if your degree of self-criticism is so high that you feel there is no hope? A study in South Korea was done with highly self-critical individuals to see if a loving-kindness compassion program could affect cardiac function as measured in heart rate variability. The study showed that, even when high levels of self-criticism are present, HRV levels can be improved through compassion practices.[12] How cool is that?

Personally, I love it when science reinforces intuition. We know compassion is good. We know this at a visceral level. Now, we are seeing that not only is compassion good for us, but it is also a lifesaver.

As I always tell my patients, "You got more going right than wrong." When they ask how I know this, I reply, "You are still alive."

You're still alive. Start there.

Chapter Four

COMPASSION AND THE BRAIN

"The compassionate mind is the mind that transforms."

– Paul A. Gilbert

COMPASSION MAY SEEM more like a heart-centered state than a mind-centered one. However, compassion is a full-body experience. The brain is indeed affected and transformed through acts of compassion. Our brains are also changed by traumatic events, and when these traumatic events take hold of our brains we may find ourselves in situations where we become triggered.

Every human being has triggers. Being triggered—something all of us experience in our lives and especially in the type of work we do—is a good way to begin the discussion of compassion and the brain.

I want to talk about triggers in a way that makes scientific and emotional sense. The word "trigger" has been overused and weaponized in a way that I don't believe is healthy or useful. So, let's define what a trigger actually is, and what happens in the body when it occurs.

Triggers are circumstances and/or situations we encounter that set off physical, emotional, and neurological responses. These can be traumas directly experienced, or vicarious traumas we witness or hear about. When we are triggered, our brains believe that we are under attack. Psychologist Daniel Goleman has called this "amygdala hijack." When this happens, our amygdala creates an environment in our brain where we are unable to respond with grace. Our frontal lobe receives messages to slow down (thus leaving us without a lot of logic to help us through). Often, this response is rooted in past trauma of some kind; something about the current situation or triggering element reminds us (most of the time not consciously) of an event when we were hurt or unsafe or both. Because of this association, our brain now believes we are in a life-threatening situation—even if, rationally, we know that the situation isn't actually dangerous. The brain cannot tell the difference between a real threat and an imagined or perceived threat while in a state of "amygdala hijack," and so we might act or react in ways that seem radically out of sync with the actual situations.

I also want to add that triggers, while they may range

from mild to severe, are gateways for compassionate growth as well as emotional and physical healing. When we approach our triggers with compassion, it gives us an opportunity to get closer to our suffering—and, consequently, our healing.

While I was studying compassion at Stanford, my mentor, Neelama Eyres, gave one of the most moving and convincing presentations on being triggered that I have ever seen. She invited us to sink into the richness of life, the sweetness *and* the pain, and realize that the pain of being triggered is an invitation to healing. I agree with her assessment. She cultivated her own understanding of triggers through her lived experiences and through the teachings of David Richo, who states that any word, person, event, experience, or touch has the potential to elicit an immediate emotional reaction from us.

Neelama, in her presentation, described triggering as a four-level process. This is my understanding of that process, related in my own words.

1. **Physical.** When we feel tension, we might feel a change in our internal temperature. We might breathe differently. Our muscles might tense, and we may feel our jaw tighten or shoulders rise. Our vision may narrow or sharpen. Our body has alerted us that there is a problem (whether real or perceived).

2. **Emotional.** Sadness, fear, frustration, anxiety, and anger are all common responses to being

triggered. These emotional responses will be BIG. You will not feel mild emotions when triggered.

3. **Mental.** At this level, we might feel self-judgment or blame. We may blame others for our discomfort. We may replay the story over and over, increasing our emotional response. Our minds can make up mental narratives that repeat themselves for hours or days—or even months or years.

4. **Neurological.** This is where the amygdala and our brain come in for a survival response. We are all familiar with the "flight, fight, or freeze" impulse. There's also another response called fawning, in which we might attempt to make things more pleasing to alleviate the suffering in our brain and calm our amygdala into a sense of security. This is when we act very nice to someone who triggers us. (Kill them with kindness?) Well, this does more harm than good to you when you are triggered. It is also a favorite of mine.

How does this process play out in real time—and, in particular, in a patient care setting? It can happen in myriad ways. A patient gets a diagnosis of something that caused the death of someone you love. A patient looks like someone who hurt you, or who hurt someone you love. A patient is going through something you once went through. Maybe the trigger has nothing to do with your patients at all and happened before you came to work, but still affects your ability to be present and offer compassionate care. The list of possibilities is truly endless. That's why it is critical work for each of us to learn about, and befriend, our triggers.

A personal example that stands out for me as an example of being triggered occurred while I was still in medical training. I was performing sports physicals for high school students as a side job with one of my professors. This job was fantastic because it paid $20 an hour, an unheard-of wage at the time—so, willingly I went forth.

When I performed these exams on the young women, there were certain patients to whom I had a visceral reaction. My body tightened up. I felt sick and angry. Irrationally, I often felt that I disliked these patients without even knowing them. As someone who considers herself a loving, accepting person, this was emotionally difficult for me to handle. For the first time since beginning my training, I began to tell myself that there was something wrong with me, that maybe I wasn't cut out to practice medicine.

I knew this wasn't okay, and I wanted to get some help to figure out what was going on. I went to my professor, who in turn sent me to the medical school's counselors' office.

I agreed to go to the counselors' office because they specialize in helping people who are training to practice medicine, and they're well-versed in the difficulties that we encounter when we're learning to help others heal. They know that our journey as healers also charges us with healing the deepest and most painful parts of ourselves.

The counselors' office was behind an orange door. I can still see that door clearly in my mind; it seemed to lead to another dimension. When I went through that door, I learned about an alternate reality. This reality was part of my truth—a truth I could not admit to because it was so painful.

When I told the counselor about the difficulties I was having when treating these high school-age women, the counselor asked, "Did you have a sexual experience you were ashamed of when you were around that age?"

Immediately, I knew exactly what he was referring to. I *had* had an experience like that.

I was sure the counselor was going to judge me, but I told him about the events of that night anyway. I told him how I was with friends. How we drank peppermint schnapps and were talking in the garage. How, when I became too drunk, the two boys brought me into a bedroom and put me into the bed. How they took turns on me while the other watched.

I told him how, when they were finished, they called my mom to pick me up. How I vomited all over the outside of the car while Ma told me how lucky I was to have friends who cared enough to call her. How Ma and I never spoke about that night again, but that when I saw one of my "friends" years later, he said he'd gone first because he liked me. He *really* liked me.

When I finished speaking, the counselor sat quietly for a moment. Then, he looked me in the eyes and said calmly, "Catherine, do you know you were raped?"

I was furious. This man I'd never met before had the *audacity* to call me a victim of rape. I was *not* a victim. I was strong, I was smart, and I was not going to let *anybody* take *anything* from me.

I stormed out of his office and went for a ten-mile run.

Only several months later did I feel ready to walk through that orange door again and do the hard work of looking at that night through compassionate, adult eyes.

I know now that I went through the four levels of triggering during that experience. When I saw those patients, the tension in my body was so terrible that I could feel almost a strangling of my breath. Then, my emotions kicked in. My mind picked up the loop of shame and blame and started attacking my ambitions as a medical professional. Finally, the counselor's words felt so dangerous to me that it kickstarted an amygdala hijacking— which in turn caused me to become irrationally furious and storm out of the office.

We all have traumas and triggers. When we don't recognize them for what they are, we run the risk of our triggers impacting our lives and our patient care. In the case of those teenage athletes, my patients' traumas, which could be felt and seen with an empathetic hit, triggered my own traumatic event. There was no reason for me to treat certain girls differently, but because I was triggered,

I did. Thankfully, the quality and outcome of care was not negatively impacted—but in another situation, it might have been.

We will never be able to prevent ourselves from being triggered. We are human, and as human beings we have all experienced traumas. Triggers are neurological, and they are also an invitation to heal.

So, where does compassion factor into all of this?

The brain is essential to our compassionate response, and when it is hijacked by a trigger, we are less able to offer compassionate care to others. Compassion, in particular self-compassion, has the potential to slow the response when we are triggered.

Coming to terms with my own traumatic experience and doing the work to understand my triggers transformed my practice of medicine overall, and my relationship with patients who had been raped themselves in particular. While I still get triggered in certain situations, it is no longer likely to derail me. I am able to hold space and feel a deep, abiding sense of compassion for those who have been abused. I can help them feel seen and understood because I have done the work to facilitate my own healing. However, prior to my own healing, I was at risk of further traumatizing the traumatized during every interaction.

Pay attention to what I just said. We hurt each other by not healing our wounds. We also heal each other by healing them.

It takes practice and a whole lot of self-compassion to

look at ourselves through this lens. This practice is not for the weak. However, I already know you are a warrior, since you have taken up the task of being a healer. If you want to dig deeper into turning your traumas into triumphs, consider Dr. Joyce Mikal-Flynn's outstanding work in post-traumatic growth.

Specific Areas of the Compassionate Brain

The areas of the brain associated with compassion are vast and overlapping. Most of the current studies have been performed with functional MRI (fMRI). These studies provide insight into what areas of the brain "light up" when we are in a compassionate state. This research is new and emerging but critical to the understanding of why compassion is crucial for brain health and healing.

Understand that the sites mentioned below do not act singularly. They function together. When a group of areas work together, we call it a network. Also, we are just beginning to understand the brain's capacity and complexity. The areas of the brain below may have more functions than the ones I list here; my focus is on how specific functions relate to compassion.

- **Inferior parietal cortex.** This area of the brain helps with perspective and judging social closeness between people, and also with emotional regulation.[1] Compassion training may increase this effect. When you are in a compassionate state, it is vital to have the ability to evaluate the social closeness or distance between people; this perspective helps you bring healthy boundaries into an exam room and beyond.

- **Medial orbitofrontal cortex (mOFC).** This part of your brain is in the area above your eyes. Emotion and reward-based decision-making take place here, thanks in part to the mOFC's ties to the limbic system. Reward is a repeating theme of compassion's effect in the brain. One study found that, when we practice compassion meditations, this area of the brain lights up when we perceive the suffering of others—and more, that it is possible to train the brain to do so.[2] This study also made a point to note that affinity (being attracted to or going towards something or someone) is also a function of this part of the brain. I think it's wonderful that the area associated with "going towards something" is also where a compassionate meditation practice can be viewed. It reinforces that we are wired to compassionately connect at a neuro-physiological level.

- **Dorsal medial prefrontal cortex (dmPFC).** This region is part of the prefrontal cortex, the front part of your brain right behind your forehead. The prefrontal cortex has been broken down into different parts that work as a network to help you plan and act with some goal in mind and then communicate the next logical step to other parts of the brain. Often, this part of the frontal lobe is described as the area of "executive function." Executive function includes tasks like balancing a checkbook, not saying the rude comment that you're thinking while that coworker is talking, and any other tasks that require conscious cognitive oversight. It makes sense that the frontal lobe is involved in compassion, because if you want to alleviate another person's suffering, you will need a plan! This brain area also has a role in what we think and how our thinking connects to motivated actions. It helps us to figure out our own emotions and those of others, which empowers the deep connection crucial with compassion using social inference.[3] This part of the frontal lobe Is also activated when deciding to what degree you will display altruism with another human being.[4]

In other words, it helps you help, and helps you not burn out. Very cool indeed.

- **Ventral medial prefrontal cortex (vmPFC).** The vmPFC helps us in behavioral control and moral decision-making. When we have experienced damage to this part of the brain, we are less likely to come to the aid of a fellow human being.[5] When the opportunity to help another arises the ventromedial prefrontal cortex (vmPFC) lights up.[6]

- **Nucleus accumbens (NA).** This area of the brain is quite fascinating. In fMRI studies, there is evidence of increased connectivity to this site, in particular with compassion training.[7] Interestingly, this site has a role in processing adverse experiences in learning to move away from them, and processing positive experiences. It helps us to know when to go forth, and when to hold back—distinctions that are crucial in an effective compassionate response. It also connects to the ventral tegmental area, the specific brain area which communicates with the NA via dopamine. (More reward system connections.)

- **Ventral striatum.** The nucleus accumbens (NA) is inside the ventral striatum. Prosocial behaviors[8] and reward processes occur here. In addition, when these areas work together, this part of our brain creates the desire to seek out the reward situation or substance.[9] (More dopaminergic feedback and reward!)

- **Anterior cingulate cortex.** There is a lot going on here! This part of the brain is in the middle of the brain itself, and has connections to the limbic system. This is partly where our "empathetic hit" comes from when we recognize suffering. However, with compassion training, we are able to move out the painful state of empathy toward the rewards systems.[10] Ethics, morality, and reward anticipations are dealt with in this brain area. Decision-making plays a role here, and conflict and error are processed here. When something "just doesn't look/feel right," this area of your brain works to make sense of things and lets you know when they do not. More of the good stuff we need to bring compassion forth. Finally, the pregenual anterior cingulate cortex is one of the areas that "lit up" consistently and robustly over several peer reviewed studies involving compassion.[11]

- **Putamen.** This area of the brain is often associated with movement. We know that degeneration of this area is the cause of Huntington's disease. This area of the brain is also connected to regulating emotions. We need to be grounded and regulated in a compassionate response. This area lights up with vigor with compassion training.[12]

- **Pallidum.** This area of the brain has been called the "limbic final common pathway" for the area serving along the pathway that processes multiple different reward systems in the brain.[13][14] Reward systems from every angle are being lit up with compassion.

- **Ventral tegmental area (VTA).** The VTA has branches that go to two major pathways in the brain: the mesocortical and mesolimbic pathways. These pathways enhance connections to the prefrontal cortex, the orbitofrontal cortex, and the cingulate region of the brain. These brain areas work together with motivation, emotions, and executive functioning—everything we need for an outstanding compassionate response! The VTA's connection through the mesolimbic pathway can access the nucleus accumbens and the amygdala. We know that dopamine plays a role in rewards systems in our brain, and the VTA has a high concentration of dopamine neurons.[15] When we have dysfunction in these areas of the brain, we suffer with pain, depression, and lack of motivation.[16] (Sounds like empathetic overwhelm to me!)

- **Amygdala.** While it has many protective mechanisms (as witnessed in being triggered), the amygdala also helps us assign importance to specific events and decide whether to avoid or go towards these events—again, a discernment which is absolutely needed in a compassionate response. When our reward centers are lighting up with compassion, our amygdala has no trouble assigning a green light to such events as they occur and taking the backseat as long as no danger is afoot. Our brains are more than happy to continue being compassionate, because they know when doing less gives us more.

- **Temporal parietal junction.** This area of the brain helps us to understand social inferences and understand another person's mental state. It helps us to determine the degree of suffering of another human being.[17] This work is not done in a single place. The cortical regions of the brain that also help in the ability to recognize the mental states of others also include the posterior cingulate cortex and the dorsal medial prefrontal cortex.[18] If you cannot understand what the other person is experiencing, how can you respond appropriately at all?

- **The salience network:** This is my favorite part of the brain, hands down. The salience network is the network of the brain that helps us figure out what is essential and what is not. It also helps to coordinate resources in the brain to respond to any relevant stimulus that occurs. I like to call the salience network the "ride or die" area. It's always looking out for what is relevant and helps you respond no matter the situation. It can take you from sitting in a chair zoning out (default mode network) to fully alert and ready to care for someone who is suffering.[19] That is pretty badass if you ask me!

A FEW WORDS ABOUT DOPAMINE, COMPASSION, AND EMPATHY

As you may have noticed, there are many areas of the brain involved with compassion response that are also involved with dopamine.

Dopamine helps with learning and motivation. Over the last forty years, we have begun to understand its role better. Dopamine is a neurotransmitter that sends signals throughout the brain, and it is also a catecholamine, a type of neurohormone.

If you have too little dopamine, you can end up with a disease called Parkinson's. Too much dopamine occurs with the use of certain drugs like methamphetamine.

Dopamine can affect memory, lactation, attention, sleep, and motivation. It also teaches us to go after what we want. An excellent example of this is when you have a lollipop for the first time in your life and you really enjoy it. Your brain releases some dopamine, but it doesn't really think about the lollipop. Instead, it thinks about everything that happened *before* you got the lollipop. How did you get that lollipop in the first place? The brain then recreates the situation to get the reward—in this case, the lollipop—again.

The next time you get the lollipop, the dopamine is not released in the same way because it doesn't care about the lollipop at all. The dopamine release happens when you get close to the place where you got the lollipop. When you start to eat it, the dopamine recedes. In this way, dopamine can be very motivating.

Drugs like cocaine and especially methamphetamine cause a very large dopamine release. This is different than with the lollipop, because while the dopamine hit comes right before you get the lollipop in the anticipatory phase, the larger dopamine hit from these drugs come with actual use, making them even harder to resist. The drive for the drug then becomes quite disruptive. In fact, the lack of compassion and empathy we see in addicts might just be due to their brains being overridden by the quest for more dopamine.

We know now, after learning about the brain areas and compassion, that dopamine is also associated with compassion. Performing a compassionate act or feeling a compassionate feeling elicits a dopamine release, as well as a hit of oxytocin. You get hits of these "love drugs" when you plan a compassionate act *and* when you execute that compassionate act. Double dose? Yes, please. This is why you cannot burn out from true compassion.

Now for a bit of scientific reality that you may not like.

I often see "empathy training" programs offered for hospital staff—and honestly, they make my stomach turn a bit. I understand the intent is benevolent; however, from a psychophysiological standpoint, empathy training is the *last* thing we need. In fact, most of us are so embedded in our empathy that we can hardly tolerate coming to work some days. Feeling each other's feelings can be exhausting. More, feeling our patients' feelings for longer than it takes to get an understanding of where they are and how we can help is counterproductive to healing *because it merely duplicates and enhances negative feelings.* Instead, we need to harness the power of compassion and use our natural empathetic response to motivate us to alleviate suffering rather than adding to it (as too much empathy often does).

Remember, empathy is like salt: a little is good, but too much is bad for your health.

Let's look at this from a purely scientific stance, starting with positive and negative effects.

The *negative effect* is defined as the bringing forth of negative emotions. This can be any negative emotion/outcome. For example, if you see a child crying, it may elicit a negative emotion from you, like sadness for the child or annoyance about the loud cries.

On the other hand, the *positive effect* is about bringing forth a positive emotion associated with a situation. For example, you see a rainbow, and it makes you smile.[20] These are important effects to keep in mind when talking about compassion versus empathy.

Research shows that functional neuroplasticity (how the brain changes when learning) occurs with compassion training in the medial orbitofrontal cortex, pallidum, putamen, and ventral tegmental areas. Also indicated are increased positive effects after compassion training; in increased empathy, the negative effect is more robust.[21]

This same group of researchers found very different brain patterns in compassion versus empathy. Empathy lights up the pain centers of the brain, while compassion is associated more with reward centers.[22] This effect is seen even when subjects are presented with the suffering of another human being—which clearly displays the differences between compassion and empathy. This is not just opinion; it is fMRI-researched data.

Of course, you can have an empathetic response to someone's joy and feel the joy with them; this is also empathy.[23] In medicine, we do have these opportunities, but they are far less common in clinical situations than pain and suffering.

Knowing that compassion creates pathways for both dopamine and oxytocin, we can effectively discredit the idea of "compassion fatigue." What most people call compassion fatigue is actually empathetic overwhelm or just plain ol' burnout.

Consider for a moment chronic pain patients and how the pain centers of their brain are lit up day after day. Quickly, they become depressed, despondent, and burned out. Chronic empathy may have the same effect.

Neither empathetic overwhelm nor burnout have anything to do with compassion. In fact, *true* compassion for ourselves and others, when mindfully practiced and skillfully applied, can actually counteract both of those symptom profiles and preserve our best efforts to alleviate others' suffering.

Odds and Ends of the Compassionate Brain

As I've shared, no one area of the brain is labeled or wired for compassion alone. Nor are the brain areas and systems I've discussed up to this point the only systems that light up with compassion. As we continue to research and gain insight into the incredible effects of compassion on the brain, we will have more tools to help our patients and ourselves. What I have presented here is just the beginning.

It's also important to remember that our degrees of compassion may be affected by the subject of suffering. If it's somebody we've loved for many years, and we have memories of good times, areas of our brain that we use for memory retrieval will be lit up; these areas Include the posterior inferior parietal lobe and the medial temporal lobe which includes the hippocampus. The mirror neuron system includes the posterior superior temporal sulcus, the premotor cortex, and the intraparietal sulcus. This area helps us to understand the actions of others.[24] We may even be able to learn behaviors like compassion by watching others.[25] Understanding each other is critical to a compassionate action.

EXPERT VERSUS NOVICE

I recommend keeping a curious beginner's mind in most things. Yet, there are advantages to striving for expertise. Research indicates a distinction between compassion experts and compassion novices. When we become better at expressing compassion through compassionate actions and compassionate meditations, our brain and body respond even faster.[26][27] Thus, you can be reassured that the practices I discuss in this book will get easier over time because, with repetition, your brain will put forth less effort for the same remarkable compassionate acts. The coolness of compassion just keeps on coming.

As previously stated, most of the research I've discussed was conducted with functional MRIs, which is very expensive and time-consuming. There is no good substitution for this approach at this time. However, testing done using an electroencephalogram (EEG) has also provided correlative (and much cheaper) evidence of compassion's effect on brain function. For example, we see changes in gamma waves with those who do compassion-based meditations.[28] Gamma waves are the highest-frequency brain waves that we know of. When gamma waves appear, it is usually at a time when we are feeling happy and are very thoughtful, focused, and alert. These waves are not seen when under stress or burnout. These same types of waves are seen in more significant numbers when we do a compassion-focused meditation. More gamma? I'd say that's a pretty fine reward for exercising compassion!

The research in this area is new and growing, so I expect our understanding of compassion's effect on the brain will grow and change in the years to come. At this point, the main takeaways with which I want to leave you are the following. Compassion is associated with reward systems through complex processes in our brains; and, even more remarkably, compassion can be learned to the degree that it changes our brain into a more compassionate brain. Self-compassion and compassion are natural states of being. However, our triggers can act as barriers to these states until we learn to work with them—you guessed it—compassionately.

In the following chapters, you will learn the specifics of how to express a fully embodied compassionate response without forgoing your own well-being. As you do, you will discover the compassionate warrior within you who is always ready to come forth with a healing power that rivals even our best medical interventions.

Chapter Five

THE VAGUS NERVE AND THE MIND-BODY CONNECTION

"Not all those who wander are lost."

– J.R.R. Tolkien

THOSE OF US who lived through the early days of the pandemic will always remember the panic we felt when we learned that the COVID-19 virus was airborne, and we didn't have enough protective gear to go around. We could no longer be sure that when we needed an N-95 mask it would be there, or even properly fit. Meanwhile, our safety gloves were ill-fitting and getting thinner by the day as supply and demand made us desperate for any supplies.

The atmosphere quickly shifted from uncertainty to fear.

More, the pandemic was the first time in my memory as a practitioner when no one had a real plan. Before that, when people came into the hospital to be treated, we knew what to do—and if we didn't, we knew how to find someone who did. There are always exceptions; however, by and large, this was the way we practiced. This made everyone feel safe: you have X, we do Y. Very rarely did we have to say, "We know what it is, but we have no idea what to do with it"—at least, not on such a massive scale. COVID changed that. We were trying to create a safe place for our patients to come and be seen, but we weren't sure what that meant anymore.

Then, of course, there was the human-to-human safety factor. We were asked to protect ourselves and each other by wearing masks and standing six feet apart. In the scheme of things, this seemed like a small ask, but we quickly found that not all people are capable of honoring such requests.

As the pandemic continued, we faced more anger and aggression from our patients than I had seen in over fifteen years of working in emergency departments. I was astounded at the amount of physical and psychological abuse that healthcare providers at every level endured. We had patients bringing guns into the hospital and open-carrying during visits. I felt unsafe in the office where I had practiced medicine for twenty years.

There was one patient who really destroyed my sense of safety in my own clinic. He refused to let me leave until I gave him what he wanted—which was a specific prescription that was not therapeutic for his diagnosis. This kind of thing happens all the time, but I can usually explain my viewpoint to the patient and get their buy-in. Not this time. This man escalated and became verbally abusive. He was between me and the door, so I could not simply walk out. I tried calling for help, but nobody heard. I tried sending a message through the computer and putting a red dot near the patient's name, which is an indicator that something needs to be done in the room. None of this worked. Eventually, I was able to get out of the room. The patient left in a rage before we could do anything more about it. We filed a report, but since he did not actually lay a hand on me, there was nothing to be enforced.

Being alone in a room with a patient—especially if they were male and bigger than me—became terrifying. I started carrying mace and a taser in a fanny pack, just in case I couldn't get out of the room next time.

It wasn't just men: many women were equally aggressive. They would demand what they wanted from me, despite the fact that their requests went against my best practices, and then become angry with me when I declined. I would try to provide evidence that the treatments they had discovered on Google were actually harmful, but they had no faith in my twenty-plus years of experience. They would simply argue that nobody knew what they were doing anymore, and what was the point anyway? "Just give me my (fill in the blank)."

Patients were yelling at our staff on a daily basis just for trying to take care of them. Please keep in mind that they came to us; we did not seek them out. They came for help. They came for our professional opinion—unless, of course, they didn't. That's where it got weird. They refused to wear masks in the office even when they came in with respiratory symptoms. The clinic was no longer a place where we could be our best selves. We were not safe to practice.

When we feel unsafe and our nervous systems are on high alert, we cannot provide our best care—not for our patients, and certainly not for ourselves. But when we meet anger with anger and fear with fear, we don't gain trust and peace; we gain more fear and anger. This dynamic is playing out in every corner of the medical world today. On every level—medically, socially, economically, politically—our society was not ready for what we experienced.

There is a link between fear and trauma and our ability to respond appropriately to a situation. The more fearful or traumatized we are, the less compassion we are able to uncover and express—to others, and to ourselves. That's why it's important to understand the connection between compassion and the parasympathetic nervous system. With compassion, we can diffuse some of the damaging aspects of high-intensity situations and help our bodies self-regulate to create more positive outcomes. Being the calm in the storm is imperative in these situations.

Basics of the Peripheral Nervous System and Vagus Nerve

Of all the nerves in the body, I love the vagus nerve the most. It is the vagabond, the ultimate traveler, and the one nerve that touches on more of the mind-body connection than any other nerve that exists.

How compassion and the vagus nerve interact with one another has a scientific basis, and it is also a bit of a love story.

But first, a bit of context.

There are twelve pairs of cranial nerves and thirty-one pairs of spinal nerves. These nerves make the connections between the central nervous system (brain and spinal cord) and the rest of the body.

The peripheral nervous system is composed of the somatic nervous system and the autonomic nervous system. The somatic nervous system is voluntary, and helps you do things like move your musculoskeletal system to walk, dance, or sing. It also relays information from your eyes, ears, and skin to the central nervous system. The autonomic nervous system is involuntary (automatic), and regulates many vital functions including your heartbeat, digestion, and elimination. Breathing is unique as you have both voluntary and autonomic control. Within the autonomic nervous system are three "divisions": the sympathetic nervous system, the parasympathetic nervous system, and the enteric nervous system. For the purposes of this discussion, we will focus on the first two.

It is thought that the sympathetic nervous system controls the body's organs in times of stress, and the parasympathetic nervous system controls the organs when the body is at rest. This is an oversimplified theory. In truth, they are always working together in a well-executed dance to find balance. Think Fred and Ginger— it is *that* good.

The vagus nerve is the main nerve of the parasympathetic nervous system and is the only cranial nerve that goes beyond your head and neck areas. In fact, it travels throughout your entire body to reach internal organs.

Motor fibers from both the sympathetic and the parasympathetic nervous systems innervate the heart, lungs, and abdominal wall. This helps to regulate your heart rate, breathing, and digestive processes. In addition to the aforementioned areas, the vagus nerve also innervates your spleen, liver, gallbladder, stomach, kidneys, small intestine, and colon.

The parasympathetic nervous system helps to keep the sympathetic nervous system in check. Without the parasympathetic nervous system dampening the sympathetic nervous system, (often called the parasympathetic break), your heart rate would rise, your blood pressure would increase, and the stress response from the sympathetic nervous system would go unopposed. Your parasympathetic nervous system is necessary for life.

This is where the love story begins. Your parasympathetic and sympathetic nervous systems work together to bring you into balance. When compassion is present, these effects are amplified, and greater balance arises. To me, this feels like an act of great love.

When we are overly stressed or have been traumatized, the sympathetic and parasympathetic nervous systems work tirelessly to keep us safe from harm. Sometimes, however, this "keeping us safe" goes a little too far. That's where things sometimes go awry. When our autonomic system is dysregulated, the body functions in a less-than-optimal state. Compassion can help us to regulate a dysregulated system, as measured through vagal mediated cardiac measurements of heart rate variability (HRV). However, before we dive into more research around HRV, let's discuss a concept that has evolved over the last twenty years, and which may be central to our understanding of compassion's effects on the nervous system.

POLYVAGAL THEORY

We cannot discuss the vagus nerve without discussing *polyvagal theory.* Dr. Stephen Porges is the pioneer behind this theory. Originally, he came upon this while studying heart rate variability in infants.[1][2]

As I was reading through many papers by and about Dr. Porges, I found a phenomenal lecture by his son, Seth Porges, which explains polyvagal theory and how it works pragmatically, in a user-friendly way. That lecture, along with my own extensive research, informs the following summary.

Let's begin with a term coined by Dr Porges: *neuroception*. Neuroception is your brain's way of distinguishing whether a situation or environment is safe or dangerous and informs your nervous system of the perceived threat to safety. Your nervous system will then send messages to your body to react in kind.

There are three potential messages or "states" that can occur from neuroception:

- Safe

- Dangerous

- Life-threatening

In the "safe" state, your heart rate slows down, your digestion is stimulated, your facial muscles are activated so that you can smile and increase vocalization, and you begin to make more eye contact. The middle ear muscles are activated so that you can better hear mid-range sounds, like the human voice. It's also important to note that we have an increase of oxytocin in this safe state. This creates increased connection to others, learning, critical thinking, increased productivity, and creativity; it could be considered a "flow" state. It helps us to relax and our body functions to operate appropriately. This, in turn, makes others feel more drawn toward us, optimizing our human experience.

The next state is the "dangerous" state, where the sympathetic nervous system is activated. In this state, your heart will speed up, your pain tolerance will increase, and your facial muscles will step in, giving your face a flat, unapproachable affect. The middle ear muscles turn off so that you don't hear that mid-range human voice, but instead hear more of the low- and high-pitch frequencies associated with predators.

The third state is "life-threatening." This state is beyond "flight or fight": it's shutdown. It is very reptilian in nature and is often trauma-based. When awful events occur and we wonder why we did not fight back or run, this is the reason why. It is not under our conscious control. Not understanding this automatic unconscious response has caused so much pain to victims of traumatic events.

Practically speaking, we use our neuroception when we meet new people. It helps us to determine if somebody is kind (safe) or unkind (not safe). Getting it wrong can be dangerous, so we have a bias to see danger even when there isn't danger physiologically. This is often called a negativity bias. It is a less-evolved part of our human makeup left over from the days when we did not have the safety of consistent food, shelter, and an absence of lethal predators. The more perilous something appears to be, the less evolved our response is. The standard response to an event which your body perceives as "life-threatening" is to shut down or "play dead"—which, as noted above, is involuntary.

Your vagus nerve is what conveys this neuroceptive information to your body and initiates these states.

In the polyvagal theory, the vagus nerve has two branches associated with it. (Hence, the name *poly*vagal.) Both branches send messages from the central nervous system to the peripheral nervous system. One branch is myelinated (fast like a freeway), and the other is unmyelinated (slow like an off-road mountain path).

The myelinated branch is ventral. It is more recently evolved than the dorsal by about 300 million years. It sends the messages when we are in the safe state. These messages go quickly and slow you down in a "good" way—lowering your heart rate and enabling you to take a nice, deep breath. You can then feel connected, grounded, and joyful. Then, you can respond appropriately to the stimuli at hand. This response is more evolved to the "safe" world we live in, and is activated in states of compassion.

The dorsal unmyelinated branch is primitive, having evolved about 500 million years ago. It sends messages more slowly when we are in the life-threatening state. When this branch is active and your psyche sees no way out, you will slow down, disassociate, go "numb," or shut down in preparation for death. Your body will increase endorphins that help to numb pain, or at least increase your threshold. The dorsal branch decreases blood pressure, temperature, and muscle tone.

The more traumatic events you have in your past, the more quickly and automatically the unmyelinated portion of the vagus nerve will send messages to the rest of your body. With repeated or frequent trauma, your parasympathetic nervous system becomes conditioned to sense and react to danger—physical, emotional, psychological, or otherwise.[3]

Polyvagal theory and compassion research overlap with HRV research in interesting ways, particularly as some measurements of HRV also give us information about vagal tone.

A 2015 review by Stellar et al., discusses four different studies displaying that respiratory sinus arrhythmia increases when participants are exposed to events that lead to a compassionate response.[4] As we've learned, respiratory sinus arrythmia is a phenomenon of our heart rate rising as we inhale and lowering when we exhale, and has been utilized much like HRV to measure parasympathetic tone. (RSA and HRV are more like cousins than twins; HRV gives much more precise information and many different variables to measure.) In each of these studies, parasympathetic tone increased with compassion being elicited. The authors are hesitant to say that one specific area is affected by compassion more than another, but it seems that a whole-body network creates this response to compassion with varying degrees of effect from different systems.[5] I love being able to tell people that compassion is a full-body experience.

In 2020, a meta-analysis showed vagal effect through compassion training with changes in vagal tone measured through HRV measurements.[6]

Another study from 2012 reinforced this effect of compassion on the systems affecting HRV. Researchers found that by simply receiving compassion the subject's autonomic nervous system calmed the body. In fact, this study showed that when a participant is present in the same room with a practitioner meditating on loving-kindness compassion towards the participant, the participant's heart rate slowed and breathing deepened when compared to a control group.[7] To me, this is a good argument for being careful of the company we keep.

What does this mean to you in practical terms? It means that compassion can and does have an effect on the health of your cardiovascular system. Through compassion, we have the power to change how our autonomic nervous system engages with our cardiovascular system. By engaging in compassionate activities, meditation, actions to help others, and (just as importantly) actions to help ourselves, we get a double benefit: the benefit of compassion for compassion's sake, and the calming, heart-healthy physiological response. We can live within the love story of our autonomic nervous system with its best and most perfect companion: compassion.

THE NEUROBIOLOGICAL LINK

One last mention of the "love story."

There is a neurobiological link between compassion and love that exists between the limbic brain system and reward circuits. This creates more ease between self-regulation, social contact in general, love, attachment, and compassion.[8]

Our bodies are wired for love and compassion. But in medicine—especially over the last several decades—we have been going against our innately compassionate inclinations.

According to the polyvagal theory, we all need to feel safe to perform well. We need to feel safe to live our best lives. It makes sense: when compassion and our nervous system work together, we find a place for love and health to blossom.

That said, there are different degrees and forms of "safe" when it comes to working in a hospital.

For example, there is sanitary safety. Did we autoclave the instruments to keep the sterile field sterile? Do we have proper protective gear to meet the challenge at hand?

Then, there's people safety. Are we working together or against one another? Do we feel safe with our patients, and do they feel safe with us?

Then, there's psychological safety. Will others recognize that we are doing our best, even if we don't have all the answers?

Then, finally, there's the safety we create within ourselves. Are we being kind to ourselves at the end of the day, or are we beating ourselves up for situations over which we had only partial control or no control at all?

In such a "dangerous" environment, compassion can make a huge difference.

There are two things I want you to take away from this chapter: one, that even the smallest amount of compassion can be of practical benefit by reducing the "dangerous" and "life-threatening" neuroception responses; and two, that you can and should trust your body's wisdom.

I suggest the following experiment: choose people who compassionately care for you. When you spend time together, do not pay attention to what they are doing or saying, but rather how they make you feel. We know now that even being in a room with a compassionate person can help us regulate our own nervous systems. Notice who those compassionate people are for you, and where you can be that compassionate person for someone else. Take time to slow down and make friends with your body so that you can relax when in the presence of compassionate friends and colleagues. Notice opportunities to give to others and yourself the kind of loving-kindness that heals.

Don't give your energy away willy-nilly, and be careful how you deliver compassion with people that cause harm. In these times, listen to your body; it will communicate with you and guide you on the path of true compassion that includes yourself.

That being said, embody and give your compassion with wild abandon every chance you get.

Just one small step: that is how we start.

You can do this. I believe in you.

Chapter Six

COMPASSION AND THE IMMUNE SYSTEM

"Before you heal someone, ask him if he's willing to give up the things that make him sick."

– Hippocrates

WE ALL HAVE PATIENTS that we don't want to see, don't like to treat, or find exceptionally difficult to deal with. For some of us, it's drug addicts. For others, it's the "frequent fliers." Sometimes, you just feel like if you treat one more sinus infection/UTI/flu case you will lose your mind.

If we're lucky, at some point in our careers, we will have to face who or what we find uncomfortable or off-putting, and we will make it to the other side. We will make peace with them/it/ourselves. When that happens, the thing that we resisted or brought us suffering will bring us a degree of satisfaction, understanding, or maybe even joy. Most of all, it will bring us compassion.

It might surprise you to learn that my least favorite patients have, until recently, been perimenopausal females with myriad complaints that neither they nor we can figure out. When I began encountering this type of patient, I was young and inexperienced. I found it difficult to treat these individuals because I couldn't relate to them—and, because, quite frankly, I was afraid of becoming one of them. This combination was particularly unhelpful to any middle-aged woman who came to see me with vague complaints.

Then, in my early forties, I began having new allergic reactions to several things, including various foods and environmental elements. It all felt weird and random, without rhyme or reason. To be honest, I thought I was losing my mind.

I was diagnosed with eosinophilic esophagitis—an issue of my immune system attacking my esophagus when exposed to an allergen (and there were many). I felt like I could no longer eat, drink, or even breathe air at times. My immune system had taken a turn, and my body was in full-on revolt. Multiple drug reactions and food intolerances reared their ugly heads during this time of chaos.

With all the allergies came a host of gastrointestinal symptoms. As a result, I needed to have a CT scan with contrast. While on the table, I started to feel unwell. I noticed a bunch of hives near the IV site, so I called for the nurse.

"I don't think this is going very well," I observed.

She called the physician, who immediately started putting drugs into my IV to stop the reaction.

I began passing in and out of consciousness. I could feel the sternal rub as he tried to bring me back every time I passed out.

I don't remember everything, but I do very clearly remember asking, "Am I going to die?"

"I don't think so," the physician replied.

After that, I was *certain* I was going to die, because the only acceptable answer from him at that point was "*No!*" His non-committal response was the nail in my psychological coffin.

(Remember this when you talk to your patients: Your doubt may be small, but their faith in your abilities is huge! Every nuance of how you communicate with them matters.)

Needless to say, I survived this event. I did not leave my son without a mother, my husband without a partner, or my Ma without a daughter. But something was left on that table for a very long time: my peace. I could no longer trust my body—in particular, my immune system—to do the right thing at the right time.

Before this, I had heard a lot of patients—particularly the aforementioned perimenopausal women—talk about similar symptoms that left them baffled and desperate for answers. Their cases had always frustrated me. Now, though, something had changed. It was personal.

It's funny how, when things get personal, they become far more interesting to us.

Like many of those patients, I was in a state of perimenopause; this created a host of changes in my body that affected my entire being, including my immune system. As I moved into this new stage of life, I was also under tremendous stress. Caring for an aging parent, parenting a young child, being a good partner to my husband, and practicing medicine left me depleted. My self-compassion and care for myself were at an all-time low. Now, my body was adding another source of stress, and I hated my body for betraying me. I was a walking, talking example of how a lack of self-compassion and cumulative stress can affect the body.

I began to see with new eyes and have greater compassion for those women who came into my clinic baffled and fearful. Like me, they wanted answers about what was going on with their bodies. Like me, they weren't always getting them. Our common humanity was the birthplace of my compassion for myself in this stage of life, and for those women as well.

The truth is, we didn't know then, and we still don't know now, how to help women navigate the transition through perimenopause. We—meaning, the medical community—do not study women in this transition with great vigor. Short of prescribing hormones, there appear to be few to no treatments available. That being said, we know that estrogen can make mast cells destabilize and release histamine with greater ease, and also that histamine affects more estrogen release, which perpetuates a terrible cycle. We also know that prior trauma, anxiety, and depression affect hormonal balances, which in turn affect the immune system. It's not an all-or-nothing situation. It is all connected.

We need balance. When we are traumatized and unhealed, we are out of balance.

How does this all relate to compassion? Well, we do have evidence that stress and a lack of compassion compound hormonal imbalances and therefore affect our immune systems. I can tell you with great certainty that my low self-compassion caused me to struggle deeply while trying to handle the changes in my life and body. I longed for the body of my youth, and to come home to a place within myself where I was at peace with my body. However, until very recently, this place was both elusive and mysterious.

I'm not going to say that self-compassion would have prevented any of what I went through during that period of my life. I'm also not going to say that it wouldn't have. I believe—and current research supports—that if we are kinder and gentler with ourselves, our bodies will be kinder and gentler with us. We can bring this knowledge to the table in both our daily lives and our dealings with patients.

Over the years, my body has become less reactive. Simultaneously, *I've* become less reactive. After nearly dying on that table, I was terrified for several years, and unable to find solid ground within myself. The fear lingered and grew faster than my bravery. Now, I know that this experience was simply burning away the pieces of me that needed to fall away in order for me to reach my next level of self-compassion and compassion for others.

You may have a similar story, or know someone with a story like this. We need to continue to tell our stories to heal. We need self-compassion so we can become the healers we set out to be the day we decided to care for others.

Sometimes, those opportunities for self-compassion are gentle. Other times they're not.

Both are okay.

The Immune System and Compassion

The immune system is complex. It protects us from illness by defending against viruses and bacteria, creating or controlling inflammation, and guarding against other harmful substances. It also helps prevent cancers by killing off cancerous cells before they become a problem. It has mechanisms to bring down inflammation when it gets out of control.

Pretty incredible, right?

However, our immune system can also go awry and attack our own body—as is the case with autoimmune dysfunction, allergies, and overwhelming inflammation.

In this section, we'll learn a bit about basic immunology and explore compassion's effect on the immune system.

THE BASICS OF IMMUNOLOGY

The immune system has many different mechanisms throughout our body. Some of these we are born with, and others show up later.

The immune system we are born with is called "innate immunity." Stomach acid or mucus in the throat and nose trap bacteria or viruses before they cause harm. Our skin is a protective barrier and gives immunity through sebum production. Our cough reflex works as part of our immune system to rid us of harmful viral particles (think how much you cough when ill). These physical barriers are our first line of defense.

Crying may not seem like a way to fight disease, but enzymes in our tears help protect us while releasing emotions. (More reason to have a good cry every now and again.)

Fever is a fascinating immune response as it creates an inhospitable environment for bacteria and viruses to propagate. While most of us are trained to recommend medication to bring a fever down, it can be far more beneficial to let that fever do its thing and defend our cells and organs (complications like febrile seizures aside). As in all things, the body works holistically, with all its parts in concert.

In addition to innate immunity, there is acquired or adapted immunity, which includes humoral and cellular immunities, and also passive immunity.

Acquired or adaptive immunity is obtained after being exposed to an antigen (invader). We create antibodies (warriors) that are specific to that antigen. This can occur through direct exposure to a virus or bacteria, or through immunization.

There are two types of acquired or adaptive immune function: humoral and cellular.

An antibody-driven immunity, *humoral immunity* is extracellular. This means that it occurs *outside* of the cell. The name is derived from a medieval term for body fluid called "humor." The primary mediator is the B cells (although helper T cells work here too). These B cells make antibodies (warriors) against the antigens (invaders). This is a rapid response. Humoral immunity is responsible for many hypersensitivity (allergic) reactions. Humoral immunity can also fight against cancer.

Conversely, *cellular immunity* occurs *inside* the cell. Cellular immunity is primarily a T cell-mediated response. The main components are helper T cells, natural killer cells, macrophages, and cytotoxic T cells (killer T cells). The response is to kill any cell invaded by a virus or bacteria. This response also occurs against tumor cells and transplanted cells. The onset is delayed. Protection against fungus and certain types of hypersensitivity reactions are mediated here.

We have *passive immunity* as infants because it is given

to us by our mothers. Passive immunity antibodies don't typically last for longer than twelve months. Another way to gain passive immunity is through the injection of an anti-serum that already has the antibodies present. (Post-rabies exposure treatment is anti-serum-based.)

Why all this talk about the immune system? Well, as it turns out, stress can decrease our immune system's ability to fight infection. Because our immune system does not know the difference between emotional stress and physical stress, the chemical responses for both are similar and can knock us out of balance and create inflammation where none is needed.

Consider the gravity of this. Inflammation is at the root of most of the chronic diseases we suffer from today. Stress, as perceived by our immune system, is nothing more than another invader that needs to be stopped. Our immune system uses inflammation to kill invaders and heal the body. Therefore, whenever we are in any state—emotional or physical—that is not our natural state, our immune system is activated.

Let that sink in for a moment. If our immune system is activated when we are under stress, this means *stress is not a natural state*. Stress can be a tool to motivate at times, but that is not what I am talking about here.

After surviving a global pandemic and all of the unnatural ways we were forced to be in order to protect ourselves and each other, our immune systems have been hijacked. As a result, we are seeing more inflammatory illnesses than ever before.

Let's dive a bit deeper.

STRESS AND THE IMMUNE SYSTEM

There are hundreds, possibly thousands, of research studies that have determined that psychological stress affects our human immune system. Over the last thirty years, the research has become more frequent and detailed.

The immune system is a perfect example of how the mind and body are connected. Initially, when there is a perceived stressful event, the amygdala (emotional center) talks to another area of the brain called the *hypothalamus* (the bossy town gossip telling everyone what is going on and what to do about it). The hypothalamus communicates with the rest of the body, giving signals to let the body know what to do next.

The most common responses, of course, are fight or flight. Communication with the autonomic nervous system in this state activates the sympathetic branch. This causes increased breathing, blood pressure, and heart rate, which in turn allows our lungs to use oxygen more efficiently as our body prepares to escape the perceived threat. The adrenal glands are then activated. A catecholamine called *epinephrine* is excreted and creates a cascade of biochemical events. Glucose is released for quick energy.

All of this happens before we are even aware.

The second part of the stress response is known as the *hypothalamic-pituitary axis* (HPA). This is when the *corticotropin-releasing hormone* (CRH) is released. CRH is like your high school best friend who will back you up when everyone else has left. CRH signals the pituitary gland that releases *adrenocorticotropic hormone* (ACTH). ACTH is your high school best friend's older sister, who does not mess around. This hormone goes to the adrenal glands to release cortisol.

In a typical situation, the stress recedes, and chemicals like epinephrine and cortisol return to normal levels. However, cortisol levels can stay high when the stress is ongoing, leaving your sympathetic nervous in a state of perpetual activation.

Cortisol is a bit of a double-edged sword. You can think of cortisol as a sweet aunt who's good to stay in your house for a day or three, but who starts to cause problems when she hangs around too long.

In the short term, cortisol is an anti-inflammatory agent that prevents your immune response from getting out of control. But over time, if cortisol levels remain high (as is very common with chronic stress), it puts the immune system at a disadvantage and prevents it from fighting infections and inflammation the way it would in a healthy, non-stressed environment.[1]

Interleukins

An essential part of cellular immunity, interleukins are a type of cytokine. They tell the immune system how and when to do their job in our bodies. Interleukins were named because we thought they communicated only between leukocytes. However, now we know that there is much more communication between interleukins and other types of cells. Simply stated, interleukins are communicators between cells made up of proteins. I often think of Radar from the TV show M.A.S.H. when I think of interleukins. He, like our interleukins, had the ability to communicate very clearly and with great accuracy across many differing relationships.

Interleukins are very important in inflammatory processes, including pro-inflammatory and anti-inflammatory events.[2]

Research about interleukins and their relationship to compassion is growing. Each interleukin is named with a number and has a job to do. Their functions have redundancy systems—which is helpful if you think about it. No one wants to go into a war against a pathogen alone.

Interleukin-6 (IL-6) is the interleukin most studied with compassion. IL-6 is a quick-acting response to help the body's defense. It communicates with the immune system and stimulates acute phase responses. When this interleukin is called upon by chronic issues and repeated insults, the body remains inflamed and high levels of IL-6 are seen in many inflammatory and autoimmune disorders. In fact, we have developed drugs to mediate the IL-6 response so it does not get out of control.[3]

IL-6 is also responsible for the rise of *C-reactive protein* (CRP). CRP increases when the body has an infection, trauma, malignancy, allergic reactions, and inflammation in acute (immediate) phases. When CRP levels are elevated over long periods, it leaves us more vulnerable to diseases, including diabetes.[4]

Compassion may be a viable way to decrease the robust responses of IL-6 and CRP. Research is showing some promise in this theory. Reduced measures of stress-induced IL-6 were found in individuals who received compassion meditation training,[5] especially with those who practiced more. It seems the more compassion you experience, the more robust the effect.

Fibromyalgia can be a challenging ailment to treat. However, fibromyalgia patients using compassion-based therapy decreased their IL-6 and CRP levels (and felt better) compared to controls.[6]

In 2020, a study showed that patients with COVID-19 who displayed elevated IL-6 and CRP had poor outcomes compared to those who did not.[7],[8] Could compassion help with the devastating impacts of severe COVID? If we implement this training early on in our healthcare system, could we help to save lives? Currently, there are no studies involving compassion and its impact on COVID-19, so these questions remain unanswered.

We already know from Chapter Five that just being in the room with a compassionate person calms our nervous system. So, can it also protect our immune system during acute illness? More research and time will tell—but I'm betting compassion can do it.

Compassion Meditation and Immune Function

Participants in a study were instructed with compassion meditation. The compassion meditators had lower levels of IL-6; the more they practiced, the more significant the associated drop in IL-6.[9] The researchers showed that, when stressed, the compassion meditation group's IL-6 levels did not rise as high as those who did not learn compassion meditation.

This means that overall and under stress, compassionate meditation helps calm the storm of IL-6. This gives us hope and direction for future research.

Self-Compassion and Immune Response

Not only does compassion meditation help, but self-compassion also is a predictor of IL-6 responses in acute stress. Researchers performed a two-day study to look at IL-6 after exposure to a standardized stressor in a lab setting. Day one showed lower levels of IL-6 in those who scored high in self-compassion. People with low self-compassion rates had a significant rise of IL-6 on both the first and the second day.

The second-day rise was impressive and may have been related to negative self-rumination, anticipatory stress, and lack of self-compassion. This second-day rise was not seen in the high self-compassion group.[10]

Compassion Training and
Salivary Alpha-Amylase

A component of human saliva has been used to indirectly measure sympathetic nervous system activity. When the sympathetic nervous system is in overdrive, salivary alpha-amylase will increase.[11][12] Another study showed that salivary alpha-amylase decreases occurred in those with higher levels of self-compassion, as measured by Dr. Neff's compassion score questionnaire.[13]

Brief training in self-compassion in women showed diminished salivary alpha-amylase (a measure of sympathetic activation) but not salivary cortisol (a measure of HPA axis activation) in laboratory stress response.[14]

Why is lowering alpha-amylase important? Salivary amylase is part of our mucosal immunity, true. But too much of a good thing is the theme of an overactive immune system, and alpha-amylase is no different.

Higher cortisol and alpha-amylase levels have been found in depressed individuals compared to non-depressed individuals.[15] High levels of alpha-amylase are a predictor of dental disease.[16] This leads to the correlation between poor dental health and cardiovascular disease.[17] In addition to this, elevated salivary alpha-amylase levels have been witnessed in women with cardiovascular disease, showing a link between cardiovascular events and an overactive sympathetic nervous system.[18]

Compassionate Interventions and Responses to Trauma as They Affect Immune System Function

To summarize: we have stress-activated immune systems, and elevated immune markers appear to come down with compassionate interventions. So, is there a way to slow progression or even prevent these stress responses of our immune system *before* damage is done?

Children with early-life adversities (ELAs) have displayed increased levels of salivary C-reactive proteins and other inflammatory markers that persist into adulthood.[19] Also, children with ELAs have higher rates of cardiovascular issues and immune function later in life. The term adverse childhood events (ACEs) is also used to describe this type of trauma.

An entire population of traumatized, adversely affected children will grow into adults who have a decreased ability to fight infection, a reduced ability to ward off cancer and cardiovascular disease, and a higher risk of diabetes.[20] All of these conditions came about through circumstances that were essentially out of their control.

Could compassion be a part of the solution and help heal traumatic childhood events? Preliminary research shows that cognitively-based compassion training can reduce salivary C-reactive proteins even in populations with adverse childhood events in foster care programs through childhood and adolescence.[21]

This is big news. The studies also show that the more

compassion-based knowledge and training that people have and practice, the more robust the benefit to the immune system without habituation.[22][23][24]

In the study mentioned in Chapter Three, women were studied with alpha-amylase responses to social threats. Remember that alpha-amylase has been used to predict the sympathetic nervous system response. This study showed that, after receiving a brief self-compassion training program, the participants had a less robust increase in salivary alpha-amylase when faced with a social stress test when compared to controls.[25] Short of changing the world environment for women (which will take time), we have little to aid women in dealing with the types of stress they encounter in social situations; this research could point the way to healthier strategies for women as they navigate their lives.

And what about caregivers as a subject group? Caregivers are typically an afterthought when compared to the person suffering the illness—if we think about them at all. We do so little for those who care for others. We also do so little for ourselves in our roles of caregiving. What does the research say about all of this?

In a study done in 2021, Rachel Hennein and her colleagues found that healthcare workers were suffering from increased rates of PTSD, alcohol abuse, major depressive disorders, and generalized anxiety disorder.[26]

In the medical field population, we found that certain risk factors put particular individuals in greater danger of these ill effects. In a review of sixteen different publications, the reviewers showed that being of female gender, younger age, and newer to the medical field put subjects at an increased risk for having post-traumatic stress symptoms through the pandemic. This gives us insight on those who may be more affected.[27] Also, it gives us a targeted population to help.

We knew this collective trauma was coming in late 2020, when a review of nineteen studies appeared that included three research papers from the beginning of the COVID pandemic and past research from the SARS outbreak in 2003 and the 2013 MERS outbreak. We have seen the damage that mass illness can do to our fellow healthcare providers; much of that harm could have been prevented with compassionate interventions. These studies showed that gender, marital status, time on the job, how much social support we had (think about isolation and lockdowns), and the ways we cope with stress had effects on those who were at greater risk of PTSD symptoms during these trying times.[28]

We were ill-equipped to handle any of these crises. But really, how *could* we have been prepared? Our culture does not prioritize the kindness and compassion for one another that would help us handle everyday challenges, let alone public health crises of this magnitude.

Could we really mitigate acute and chronic illness through compassion? Could we mitigate the adverse effects on our bodies and immune systems after traumatic events? Could we reduce the burden on the healthcare system by creating better health through compassion?

Could we minimize the side effects of medications by reducing our need for them?

If we can bring about even a mild to moderate decrease in stress-producing biological changes that affect our immune system to help it fight disease and positively regulate itself with compassion and self-compassion training, is it not worth trying?

The remainder of this book will be dedicated to that very effort. In upcoming chapters, you'll learn how to apply compassion to your daily life so you can reap compassion's incredible benefits in real time.

We do not have any time to lose. We have already hit the tipping point, and we have come to a moment of choice. Right here, right now, you can begin to make changes that not only bring you greater well-being but also have a lasting effect on those you care for—including your family, your friends, and your patients. Helping another can be far more motivating than helping ourselves at times, and that's where we hit the jackpot with compassion, because helping ourselves *is* helping others.

Chapter Seven

CULTIVATING COMPASSION: THE FOUNDATION

"Knowing is not enough; we must apply.
Willing is not enough; we must do."

– Goethe

WHEN MY BIOLOGICAL mother (the woman I knew as my sister growing up) passed away suddenly in her sleep, I was so grief-stricken that I could barely get out of bed. I drank more wine in the following three-year period than I had in my entire lifetime—or any other lifetime that I am aware of. It was my dark night of the soul.

Relationships with men were difficult, relationships with my friends were just as difficult, and relationships within my family were even worse. But my relationship with myself proved the most difficult of all.

In the middle of this, I'd finally had enough of so many things, but especially the disrespect and abuse I was receiving working in the emergency room. After my attending physician was verbally abusive to me, I looked at the sliding glass door of the ED, and I knew it was time. I walked out in the middle of my shift. (I both do and don't recommend this.)

After leaving that job, I had some time on my hands. I read a few books about meditation and self-compassion; notably, Thubten Chödrön's *Buddhism for Beginners* and Pema Chödrön's *The Places That Scare You* and *When Things Fall Apart,* which made me feel like an expert in Buddhist meditation. Clearly, I was *not* an expert at that point, but these books helped me become aware that there might be a better way to deal with my internal and external chaos. So, I decided to sign up for a meditation retreat at a Buddhist retreat center in Marin County, California. It just so happened that one was available in just a week or so—so, I packed my bag and drove myself out to Spirit Rock Meditation Center.

Spirit Rock was gorgeous and inviting. Its green hills, peaceful surroundings, and tranquil people all embodied the peace I sought. *This is exactly what I need,* I thought. *If I can just get over my mother's dying, the rest of my life will go back to normal.*

I was in for a rude awakening.

During this retreat, we were supposed to remain silent. We were asked not to talk on our phones, or even write in our journals. Even eye contact between participants was discouraged, as eye contact is a way of connecting with fellow human beings, and this time was intended to help us go more deeply within ourselves.

Thirty-four-year-old me thought she was ready for this.

To be honest, the first day was fine. Good, even. I was sent to a building named "Equanimity." I had no idea what the word meant—but I soon learned that it means "holding all things as equal." This doesn't mean that you don't care if good things or bad things happen; rather, equanimity gives you the freedom to stop identifying events as *only* good or *only* bad.

Was my mother's death absolutely bad? Was it absolutely anything?

I had requested a solo room since I had no desire to share sleeping space with someone I didn't know. Looking back, it's funny how, even when I was in the room by myself, I was sharing a space with somebody I didn't know. I was a stranger to myself in so many ways.

During the retreat, participants were assigned a job within the community. For the duration of my stay, my job was to serve as a kitchen worker. We could listen to instructions about our jobs while we were there, but we were asked to write down our questions and give them to the staffers rather than ask them directly.

Sitting in meditation for over eight hours each day wasn't as difficult as I thought it would be. Spirit Rock founding teacher Jack Kornfield is a master at guiding you gently through a process of self-compassion when your mind wanders. Over and over, he encouraged us to meet ourselves with patience and kindness. As I watched him sit with regal perfection at the head of the room, I wondered how he'd gotten there. What would it take to create such calm and stillness within myself?

I thought I was on the path to a Jack Kornfield type of peace. However, on day three, things really started to unravel. If the retreat had started off feeling like a honeymoon, we were now in divorce proceedings. What was happening in my own mind was scaring the shit out of me. I found that when my mind had free rein and nowhere to go, it tended to get a little ... paranoid. I kept having thoughts like, *Why did I even come to this place? What if these people are poisoning my food?* (Even though I was the one preparing the meals.) *What if these people are members of a cult—should I be worried?*

In retrospect, this shouldn't have surprised me. As an adopted child who found out the truth about my parents when and how I did, it made sense that I would have trust issues. That being said, the paranoia was intense and real. I *needed* to get out. So, on that third day, I packed my bags, grabbed my keys, and marched out the door. But when I got to my car, it was blocked in by another car parked behind me. I went back inside to the message board and requested that the car be moved, *immediately.* Then, I went back to my car and waited.

It took less than an hour for the car's owner to move the vehicle. She apologized kindly, with a look of concern and compassion, which gave me pause—but the doubt didn't stick. I drove out of there so fast that I left a cartoon puff of dust behind me.

In hindsight, I can picture the other car's owner watching me drive away with compassion, hoping that I had gained some insight into my own suffering during my stay.

I had, in fact, gained quite a lot, but I didn't recognize it at the time.

The first thing I did after driving away was get on my mobile phone and call my friends. The second thing I did was stop for a bottle of red wine—and I made sure I drank every drop of that bottle before bed that night.

And that, reader, was my first true experience with meditation—my first serious attempt to go beyond simply recognizing that I had suffered and continued to suffer, but to actually sit with my pain and suffering and get closer to myself. It was also my first fumbling foray into self-compassion.

Hardly an auspicious beginning, I know.

Still, once I was home and the paranoia receded, I found myself drawn back to the teachings. I read the *Tibetan Book of Living and Dying* by Sogyal Rinpoche— hardly a light read.

Game on.

In the following months and years, I learned an important truth. Self-compassion, whether gained through meditation or otherwise, will not stop bad things from happening, or prevent you from feeling pain or joy.

It will, however, bring you closer to your true self—the self that you are longing to meet again, but may not even know exists. The truth you seek lies within.

It took me some time, and lots of practice, but I did eventually come to see that the part of me which was desperate to get over her mother dying was *never* going to get over her mother dying. However, her death was one of the greatest gifts she ever gave me, in that it cleared the way for my healing.

Drowning in grief, I had no other option but to learn to love myself in a way that only a mother could.

I did, eventually, go back to Spirit Rock to complete a silent retreat, and I've participated in multiple weekend retreats there as well. I found a Buddhist therapist and saw him for years. I began to meditate regularly, trying to gain access to my own inner wisdom, beginning with just six minutes a day. Some days, those six minutes were a real struggle; to sit with myself for even that long felt like torture. My mind was so used to running away that the simple practice of stillness seemed impossible. Over time, however, I found I could sit longer—and when I could not sit, I was able to become kind with myself in a way that had initially seemed impossible.

After seven years, I thought more commitment might help, so I sought refuge at a Buddhist temple. I was given a Buddhist name. I followed my Lama's guidance for years until he—as a good Lama should—guided me right back to myself. I hold all of this with great regard and reverence as a precious aspect of who I am today.

In the twenty years since I ran away from that first retreat, my meditation practice has had times of great focus and insight, times of great pain, and times of great avoidance. Sometimes, I'll spend months just listening to guided meditations and following them somewhat superficially. Other times, my practice is deep, and I sit in awed silence observing my body, my spirit, my mind, the world, the meaning of life and love, and the interactions of all the above. But no matter what it looks like at any given time, it is still my practice. And, as I've learned over the years, any practice is good practice, especially when it leads to self-compassion.

Compassion Training

At this point, you may be thinking, "Compassion sounds terrific, but how do I even begin?"

For me, the most powerful route was through meditation. However, my biggest mistake (as you may have guessed after reading my story) is that I tried to put the cart before the horse. I wanted all the peace, clarity, and rewards of this elusive quality of compassion, but I had no idea that, in order to get there, I would first need to learn to get grounded.

So, what is this mysterious grounding thing?

"Grounding" is more than a New Age spiritual term. It's a way to describe the process of figuring out where you are—physically, mentally, emotionally, and spiritually—and then landing there. I mean, have you ever gone on a road trip without knowing where you're starting from? That would be crazy, right? The same is true for compassion. In order to *move* from where you are, you must *know* where you are.

And that's why you've got to get grounded.

While earning my PhD, I researched many types of compassion training. Grounding was a common theme and was required before starting any formal training. It really is necessary to begin with the very thing I did not do when I began my journey toward self-compassion!

With full self-compassionate disclosure, I can say that I started on the right path for me; it had so much potential! I just didn't know what I was doing—and because I didn't know, I couldn't ask the right questions to figure it out. Honestly, I couldn't have found my grounded center if it punched me in the face. It's not like they teach these things in medical training.

When it comes to grounding, unless you seek it, it will not be found. It is very simple, but not always easy, to attain this state of being. When you discover it for yourself, it will become extremely obvious why grounding and compassion go hand in hand.

Getting grounded can make or break your day, time and time again. Without a grounded place to start from, we can act in many aberrant and wild ways. If you've ever gotten to the end of your day and thought, "Why the hell did I do that?" then chances are you were acting from an ungrounded place.

If you are not in a grounded state, much of what you

may perceive as compassionate will be anything but. An ungrounded compassion practice might look like this: You keep helping and helping, trying and trying. You offer help where no help is wanted or necessary. You get stuck in an empathetic state. You get overwhelmed (which, as you now know, is not compassionate at all). Then, you end up feeling angry, resentful, and unappreciated. Yet, because you like the feeling of helping, you keep coming back for more.

None of this is truly compassionate.

When you are grounded, you're in touch with that place within yourself that is solid, reliable, focused—and, most of all, kind. This might feel backward; after all, wouldn't being compassionate help us to feel those things? Well, that's a fair statement, and when I first started to explore compassion, I certainly felt that way. But when I tried to jump into a compassionate place without getting grounded first, I ended up with less than stellar results.

As the old saying goes, hindsight is 20/20. Please learn from my mistakes. Grounded compassion is so much easier, clearer, and more effective. It comes without strings. More, once you've practiced enough to get there, it can be the most sublime experience of a lifetime.

Now, you don't have to be perfect, or even experienced, with getting grounded before building your compassion muscles through the practices in this book. However, I will say that the process of getting grounded is *the most important aspect* of living a compassionate life, because it will help us avoid the pitfalls of overdoing and burning out.

So, how do we get grounded?

The first piece is to be exactly where you are. That includes your mind, your thoughts, and your emotions. Don't let your inner gaze slide toward either the past or the future. Just be here, now, without trying to change a single thing. *Not one thing.*

How is your mind? Are you frantic, focused, calm, erratic, blissed out, or pissed off? When you figure that out (which can take some time unless you already have practice at accurately naming what you are feeling and thinking), bring in some childlike curiosity. Remember who you really are: a spectacular human being having a rich and nuanced human experience.

Then see what your body is feeling. Is it tense or relaxed? Is there pain or numbness? Do you feel cold, hot, or just right? Remember, there is no need to change or judge anything; getting grounded is about finding out exactly where you are.

This practice can be done in a matter of just a few minutes, or over a longer span. It will give you valuable information about your current capacity to plan and create a compassionate response for yourself and others. At times, you will be full of love, grace, and the capacity to give and receive. At others, you will have far less to give. Even on harder days, there is always room for compassion; there is wisdom and grace in acknowledging your tired spirit and broken heart. At such times, compassion here looks like rest and renewal, not giving more or doing more.

GROUNDING THROUGH MEDITATION

If you thought that the above grounding exercise sounded like a meditation, you are (partially) correct. It did contain aspects of certain types of meditation, along with qualities of garden-variety mindfulness (which is different from meditation). That's because one of the best ways to get grounded is through meditation. Meditation can also increase our compassionate responses to suffering.[1]

Let's start by exploring a few types of meditation for beginners. This is not an exhaustive list, but it will provide you with a great starting point.

Meditation Apps

One of the easiest ways to start meditating is to grab your mobile phone and download a meditation app.

My favorites are CALM, Insight Timer, and Ten Percent. I like CALM and Ten Percent for their user-friendliness and the fact that their guided meditations don't sound like they were read by an AI bot. Insight Timer has much more variety, with meditations ranging from three minutes to over an hour. Once you've found the app you prefer, I suggest starting with five- to ten-minute meditations. Because the length of time matters less than consistency, pick a time you can fit into your schedule every day, not just once in a while.

I will warn you that having a daily practice can be a challenge. Even after twenty-plus years of practice, getting grounded with meditation often eludes me when I need it the most; however, this is also where self-compassion begins to grow. My discomfort brings me closer to my humanness and my sometimes-uncanny ability to be distracted. Sometimes I will sit down to get grounded and come back with a fantastic grocery or to-do list—fidgeting all the while. Other times, I see the beauty of our world, the people in it, and myself so clearly that it breaks my heart into a million pieces that capture the light and make rainbows all over my soul. May getting grounded do all this and more for you.

More Meditation Practices

When you are ready to move beyond your phone, here are a few suggestions for expanding your meditation practice.

- Loving-kindness meditations (Maitri) are accessible online and through the aforementioned apps. This gentle style of meditation can foster both self-awareness and self-love to create a rich place for compassion to grow. See Chapter Nine for an example script.

- Tonglen is an example of a more advanced type of loving-kindness meditation. I describe a Tonglen practice in detail in Chapter Nine.

- Your local yoga studio may have classes, workshops, or suggestions. In fact, a yoga movement practice can be a type of meditation if you find the right teacher.

- Mindful.org has a mindful directory where you can search your city to find assistance.

- Lojong is a series of Mahayana Buddhist slogans separated into seven points (or topics) that you can follow and/or meditate on; these seven points are the instructions to live a life on the path to enlightenment. If "enlightenment" sounds too daunting, rest easy: Lojong can also help anyone dig deeper into their motivations and habits. I really love Pema Chödrön's "Compassion Cards" for this: just pull one card a day and meditate on the slogan.

Then, when you want to get a little more formal:

- Mindfulness-Based Stress Reduction Program (MBSR). This was Jon Kabat-Zinn's claim to fame and quite a popular program. It's very accessible, secular, and inexpensive, making it a great place to start.

- The International Mindfulness Teachers Association. You can learn to teach mindfulness or find teachers near you.

- Spirit Rock Meditation Center is where I got my start. I suggest vipassana (insight meditation that focuses on the body and the insight that comes with such focus) as a first program. Spirit Rock has wonderful day-long, weekend, and longer silent retreats for all walks of life.

- In New York City, check out MNDFL, a secular program that is gaining quite a following.

- The Shambhala Meditation Center of New York is a Tibetan Buddhist teaching center. In Buddhist folklore, Shambhala is a mystical place in Tibet where all residents are enlightened.

- Transcendental meditation. This became popular in the 1950s and consists of a repeating mantra that you alone use to deepen your meditative experience. You can find a teacher through www.tm.org.

CHOOSE YOUR "ANCHOR" WISELY

There is one very important point I need to address regarding some of the terminology in meditation practices. In many meditation disciplines, you will often hear the word "anchor." An "anchor" is where you bring your attention when your mind wanders, and it is a crucial component when meditating on groundedness. When you find yourself distracted (which might be pretty much every second or two on some days—it can be for me), you simply pull your attention back to your anchor and keep going.

There are many different types of anchors you can use when meditating, but one of the more frequently used is the breath. At the beginning of many practices, you may be asked to take a deep breath in, perhaps while silently reciting a mantra. The breath can be a great source for grounding for many, and I love it at times—but I do not *always* love it.

If you have found breathwork difficult, you are not alone. The psychophysiology behind taking a breath is not the same for everyone. Taking a long, slow breath activates the vagus nerve, sending a calming sensation through the body and creating a feeling of groundedness. In such cases, the breath is a useful and healthy anchor for meditation practices.

However, for folks with a complex history of PTSD, trauma, or anxiety, a paradoxical reaction to a deep breath is possible. For this population, and for some others without this history, taking that deep breath and activating the vagus nerve does send a calming wave through the body—but then, a secondary reaction emerges. When you have trauma or are just feeling excessively stressed, your brain is on the lookout for danger; this is known as a "hyper-alert" state. The amygdala sends a signal to the body that reads something like, *Are you crazy? Why are you trying to relax? Don't you see the danger everywhere?* When this happens, the deep breath that was intended to calm you instead elicits a sense of panic.

When I lead meditations, I don't often start with the breath. Instead, I bring my students into the room and orient their bodies to the space they're in. I ask them to notice the temperature of the room, the color of the walls, the feeling of their feet resting on the floor. Then, I invite them to be present to whatever they're feeling without trying to change it. I allow for boredom, resistance, and peace. I allow them to simply be. That's what grounding looks like at the beginning, in the middle, and at the end: the solid place you need to find in order to practice compassion. Grounded compassion is glorious.

Whatever experience you have of grounding and meditation, be patient, kind, and loving to yourself, and you will find the way to the greatest goal of all: a reunification with your own true nature. You are always the place compassion starts.

A Final Word on Grounding and Compassion

The final word? *Equanimity.*

Equanimity can be very tricky concept. It is also very simple—but just because something is simple does not mean it is easy.

As I mentioned earlier, during my first visit to Spirit Rock Meditation Center I was placed in the building called "Equanimity." After my interview, the meditation leaders who read my application for the retreat intuitively understood that that was the quality I needed most to cultivate. I can tell you this with 100 percent certainty: equanimity is no joke. I have never felt more peaceful than in the moments where I have attained a state of equanimity. I have also never felt worse than when I lose sight of it.

Equanimity requires developing an appreciation for, and having gratitude for, all that is present, including our fellow human beings. (Yes, you read that right: this means cultivating appreciation and gratitude for the people and situations who bring us joy, and also for the people and situations who bring us other, less savory emotions.)

There are many programs out there that use equanimity as a central teaching in the path to self and other compassion.[2] Each will offer unique benefits; my suggestion is to go with what you are drawn to. If this sounds daunting, be patient. Remember the evidence-based benefits of these practices on all the various systems of the body. Be kind and compassionate with your journey. For me, the research showing the benefits of these practices can give me extra motivation when equanimity feels unavailable. My wish is that the information I've shared motivates you, too!

Chapter Eight

MEASURING COMPASSION

"The heart of science is measurement."

– Erik Brynjolfsson

FOR ME, as with most people, the old saying more or less applies: *If it isn't one thing, it's your mother.* But for me, it was my father(s).

I didn't know my biological father until I was forty-eight years old. The father that I knew growing up left our family abruptly when I was ten. I had no contact with him until I was an adult. Not one birthday card, not one birthday phone call, not one Christmas present.

Just … nothing.

Make no mistake—people impact one another's lives in their presence *and* their absence. Through his absence, the father I knew in the first ten years of my life taught me that I was not worthy of self-compassion, love, or many other things. Even if this was not his intention, these were the lessons I absorbed after being left as a child.

I got to know this father as an adult, and I wasn't so sure how I felt about it, but I knew there was a part of me that loved him desperately and wanted him to love me too. Even as an adult, I would always try to be on my best behavior around him—until one day, I failed.

It all started because I did not properly address an envelope sent to his fourth wife. There was nothing intentional about my error. The envelope contained an invitation to my wedding. My father asked for a new invite, corrected to her liking, which would have required me to order a hundred more invites. When I told him this, he replied, "Well, could you do it?"

The answer, of course, had to be, "No."

It was then that my anger began to come out. After so many years of trying to be "good" for him, of waiting for him, now he wasn't going to come to my wedding unless I sent his wife a new invite? This seemed like madness to me. After I got the RSVP in the mail, with the "will not attend" circled with his last name only, I called him. To be honest, I was about to fold and buy all the invites. But he did not pick up; the call went straight to voicemail. I felt the final pang of rage of all the years of waiting and wanting, the pain of watching my Ma suffer alone while trying to raise three children on her own.

I had nothing more to lose. I left a message to end all messages.

In that moment, I stopped being there for him and started to be there for myself. Whatever my shortcomings, imagined or otherwise, I knew I didn't deserve *this*.

Yes, I was the girl with no father at her wedding. Not because I did not have one, but because he didn't want to come. It was a crack in my armor that let in a bit of self-compassion. I was able to stand firm, and move forward knowing that I was honoring and protecting the most tender part of myself. The part of me that was afraid of being rejected *was* being rejected. I allowed myself to be with that and not try to change the situation by being disingenuous to who I really was. Printing out a hundred invitations and throwing out 99 of them to appease a woman who I did not really know was not caring for myself. Inside, I was a young girl who needed her father to choose me, and he couldn't. Again. It wasn't my job to change so that I could gain his love; instead, it was my job to let go and see the situation for what it really was.

Fast-forward nine years. By then, my father had divorced wife number four and married wife number five, a reputedly near-angelic woman named Margarita. Through the family grapevine, I'd been hearing encouraging things about his personal growth. I began to feel a sliver of hope.

He then told Margarita that if I apologized to him, he

would let me back into his life. I am not sure what story he told her, but I'm sure that in his telling, no part of the wedge between us was his doing. His required apology from me made me question whether all that "personal growth" had happened after all.

In the end, though, I apologized. Not for him, but for me. I called him and simply said, "Dad, I'm sorry."

He responded with, "Well, Cat, how've ya been?"

Since then, we have managed to grow closer. I don't think we will ever be as close as I want us to be, but it's better than the alternative: no contact, no compassion, no forgiveness, and a whole lot of anger. My apology was an act of compassion for both my dad and me, and it opened my heart in a way that I can't describe. His insistence on an apology was a gift from him to me, wrapped in some interesting packaging. When I made that phone call, I realized something critical about both of us: inside, he was still a young boy who just wanted to be seen and acknowledged. Inside, I was still a little girl who just wanted to be loved by her dad. We were seeking the same things: to be seen, loved, and met with compassion.

I also recognized that Margarita loved him so well, so deeply, and with so much compassion that he was able to grow into a better man. If love and compassion can do that, I'm all in.

Sadly, Margarita passed away in 2022. I sat with my dad in the room as we removed the life support, and I held him as he cried. I couldn't take away his pain, but I could hold him while he felt it. Holding space is an enormous act of compassion. Sometimes doing nothing is doing everything. While it might not appear so from the outside, my father is tender-hearted and sensitive; watching his beloved die was too much. There was a moment while she was passing when he wanted to leave, but there was no running away from this. Letting him leave would not have been compassionate, so I helped him sit back down. Yes, staying was painful—unbearably so—but it was also necessary, because Margarita did not die alone. We sat with her for her journey home, and neither of us will ever be the same.

I was able to give my father what I wanted from him. When things got tough, I stayed.

None of this would have happened without forgiveness and compassion. That type of compassion is badass-warrior compassion, because it comes in without compromising self and holds up what needs to be held. I will always be grateful for the lessons my dad gave me, both in his absence and in his presence. He is, like me, human.

Remember this: when people claim compassion is soft in a derogatory way. Compassion can be soft, like a warm blanket on a cold winter day, but it can also be fierce like a fire to keep you warm.

Then, there's my biological father, James Ellison.

James is one of the most kind-hearted, sensitive people I've ever met in my life. We had our first conversation just a few years ago, when I was forty-eight, six months after Ma died. (I have a feeling she orchestrated the meeting to make sure I would be okay without her.)

Through genetic testing, I found a cousin, and he helped me contact my father. My father did not know I existed until I contacted him. The first thing that he said to me was, "How does it feel to be loved by someone you've never met?" I felt these words in my bones and my soul. After all my years of trying to prove that I was worthy of love, to hear what this man said broke down barriers around my heart that I cannot describe in words.

James brought me into a whole new family. The first conversations I had with my two sisters, Emilia and Chelsea, were like talking to old friends. The first time I met my aunts and uncles, I felt loved. The welcome I received from my sister's mother, Sara, was gorgeous. They accepted and loved my son and husband as their own. At first, I questioned it; I had not done anything to deserve that love. Then I wondered something deeper: *Why does this surprise me so much*?

Growing up, only Ma had loved me unconditionally. Others, including my biological mother, would refuse to speak to me if I didn't behave the way they wanted me to. But Ma loved me even at my worst. She was strong enough to hold space for the totality of me. Again, strength is a central theme in compassion and love. In case you are wondering, this *is* what love looks like. It is also what compassion looks like. It is not conditional; it does not punish you for being human, being imperfect, or making mistakes.

I'd like to note that it's okay to take time and space away from abusive behavior. Sometimes, living at a distance is also a compassionate act, and one I have chosen with a few people in my life. My choice to step back does not mean there is no love for them; it just means there is love for me.

I think Ma really would have liked my paternal family, because they love me the way she did: with a full heart, loving all my bits.

Today, I measure compassion and self-compassion in many ways. One of them is my ability to forgive myself for not being available to people who have hurt me. Letting people in who love me even when I am not perfect is a measurement of my growth with self-compassion. Allowing people to be who they are *at a distance* when needed is a measurement of my compassion for both others and me.

This is a lifelong practice. There are stumbles and setbacks. The best way to measure progress in these areas is to look at years, not moments. The ease with which I now allow myself to be imperfect (and forgive myself for not being able to access this all the time) is my ultimate act of measurable self-compassion. How do I know this is happening? I feel less shitty about myself.

Compassion is a journey, not a destination. It will take you to places where your heart will expand beyond your wildest dreams. I know it has for me.

Putting Compassion in Perspective

There were many days in my younger years (and honestly, sometimes still in my current life) when I would look at the world and wonder, *What the fuck?*

Sometimes, I could not believe the ways in which people treat each other. They lie for all kinds of reasons. They hurt each other physically and emotionally. They steal money, property, and even little bits of our souls. They cheat in business, in relationships, and even in silly games.

I also knew (and still know) that people can be quite lovely. They will give you the shirt off their backs in the middle of a snowstorm. They will come to your aid, even if they don't know you from a hole in the wall. They love deeply, and the power of that love is transformative and redeeming.

When people ask me what brought me to study compassion—what made me so obsessed with it that I would, in my fifties, go back to school to earn a PhD and try to measure the effects of compassion on the brain and body—I tell them the truth: it was *anger*.

That confusion, that "what the fuck" feeling, made me *mad*. Yes, my trauma, grief, and family upbringing led me toward self-compassion, but my anger ultimately pushed me toward teaching compassion as a remedy for this painful emotion and the ways in which it transforms human life. I spent years trying to understand how compassion could be both so lacking and so abundant, sometimes in the same people at different times! In the end, I had to stop intellectualizing the problem, and instead get closer to it—much as I had done with my own mind through meditation.

As happens in life, I didn't completely *decide* to find

and study compassion; rather, compassion found and studied me. It demanded that I learn how and when to apply it. It shook me to my core, placed me front and center with myself, and showed me the way home to me.

Before learning the truth about compassion, I often thought of myself as a compassionate person. Many people would have said I was the most compassionate person they knew. They were wrong. What looked like compassion to them was me searching desperately for love and acceptance. I was struggling to keep my shit together. I would let anyone in free of charge. I would do just about anything to get that love and acceptance—up to and including sacrificing myself on the altar of others' needs.

A lot of us in the medical field are this way. Practicing medicine gives us an outlet to love people from a distance—which feels quite a bit safer than loving people up close. I always longed for that up-close love; it took me forty-eight years, finding my husband, giving birth to my son, and meeting my biological father and paternal family to find it. I'm not saying all these people are perfect, and neither am I, but we are perfectly imperfect together, and I am accepted in a way I have never been before. This, in turn, has allowed me to accept myself in a way I have never been free to do. I needed to find this unconditional love and acceptance in order for me and self-compassion to get down on the mat and do some wrestling.

Today, I have found a deep and abiding compassion for all the years when I struggled and searched and ached for the love I now receive.

My husband, son, and Ellison family have become my personal barometer for assessing compassion and self-compassion, along with love. If it feels like resting in a hammock on a perfect fall day, it's compassion and love. If it feels like laughing with my Ellison family, I know I am on the right track. If it adds to my life and does not subtract from it, it is the right direction. Admission into my life now has a price, and that price is love and compassion. If it feels any other way, it is *not* compassion, it is *not* love, and it is *not* making its way into my inner circle.

It's more complicated than that, of course—but in some ways, it's also that simple.

Measuring Compassion in Your Life

So, how will *you* know when you have developed compassion and learned to use it in your life? And how will you measure success?

Measuring compassion in the real world is, unsurprisingly, quite subjective. How compassionate are you? How compassionate are others around you? And who is qualified to judge what compassion is, and what it isn't?

When I teach and give lectures about compassion, I don't tell people I'm going to help them be more compassionate. If I did that, they might feel insulted, and with good reason. No one wants to hear that they aren't compassionate enough—especially people who have trained and dedicated their lives to caring for others. Instead, I share that we are *born* to be compassionate. Accessing this compassion can be tricky at times—and that's how I like to frame the work. My job is to help them learn to gain access to their innate and beautiful heart of compassion.

However, we must address this: there are times when we *believe* we're being compassionate, but we're actually being something else. Often, this is because we're confusing an empathetic response with a compassionate one, and/or practicing what I call *unskilled compassion*. Both of these responses occur when we jump so deep into the sea of others' lives that we drown ourselves. And, as we learned earlier in this book, not only is this not compassion, but it can also lead directly to burnout.

In the medical field, we have the audacity to believe that we can help people and make a difference. Often, we do—but often, we don't. Practicing compassion successfully means getting straight about what we can do for other people and what we can't, and being okay with both. (There's that pesky "equanimity" popping up again!)

This is why it's helpful to be able to measure compassion for yourself. You can use the tools in this chapter or create your own internal barometer like I did to start. I now use the self-compassion scale as a check-in for where I am and how I can grow. I find it especially helpful when I am struggling. The same may be true for you. When you're in a challenging situation, you will then be able to easily assess whether your response is coming from a place of true compassion and self-compassion or from a place of conditioned empathic response that can lead down a path of burnout and overwhelm.

When scientists asked how they could measure compassion, they first had to define it. So, when you want to measure whether an increase in compassion has occurred with you, you have many choices—but first, you must define how you see compassion showing up in your life. You can use something quite subjective such as the quality of your relationships, or the rapidity with which you are able to forgive yourself and others. A more formal approach might be to use a compassion score prior to the onset of your compassion journey, and then measure again at intervals (for example, at three, six, nine, and twelve months). Even more formal, yet not as accessible, would be the measurements of cortisol and HRV and the use of fMRIs after defined periods of regular compassion-focused practice.

The most impressive measurement of compassion for me was how I felt physically. Your autonomic nervous system will become more balanced when you can find a state of compassion for yourself and others. When I switch from a place of frustration and anger to a state of compassion, my body responds with a calm, soothing feeling. My shoulders drop, my breathing becomes slower, and my breaths lengthen and deepen. My mind slows down, and I feel less "spun out" and more focused. I also feel it in my gut—there's much less churning and gurgling.

I've said it before, and I will continue to say it: compassion is a full-body experience. If you are in tune with what your body is feeling, this is an excellent measurement of compassion. Wonderfully, if you are somebody who is not so in tune with your body, compassion can help you get there.

In my opinion, the best indicator of a compassionate life is feeling fulfilled in your relationships. This does not mean that they, or you, are perfect, only that they are perfect for you. When you have more access to ease in your human relationships than to difficulties, that is success. When your body feels more in balance than out of balance, that is success. Finally, noticing the wish to be more compassionate for ourselves and others both personally and in the work that we do is the greatest measurement of compassionate growth.

If you want a number or a scale to validate your subjective measurements, a compassion questionnaire is for you. By utilizing any number of validated questionnaires, you can measure where you are and track your own progress with a number. (What does *validated* mean? A questionnaire, to be validated, must demonstrate that it is measuring what it says it's measuring. In a compassion scale questionnaire, experts in the field of compassion decide, based on research and experience, whether the questions within the questionnaire and the score you receive actually indicate a level of compassion.)

Below, you'll find some of the best compassion measurement questionnaires out there. You can use these scales prior to and after taking a class in compassion; pre- and post-compassion exercises undertaken on your own; or, as mentioned above, at intervals along your personal compassion journey. In the assessments listed below, there are some that are very specific for particular situations (like nursing and patients' view of physician compassion).

All of the scales on this list are available online if you search them by name. The first three are my favorites (and the most validated), but investigate all of them for yourself to see which resonate most strongly with you.

- **The Self-Compassion Scale (SCS)** asks twenty-six questions with possible answers in a five-point scale ranging from "almost never" to "almost always." This scale is exciting because it picks up on both self-compassion and lack of self-compassion, emphasizing the polar nature of self-compassion as defined by Dr. Kristin Neff, who created the scale.[1][2]

- **The Self-Compassion Scale—Short Form (SCS-SF)** retains twelve items from the self-compassion scale described above.[3]

- **The Compassion Scale (CS-P)** is a twenty-four-item self-reported scale that uses a five-point Likert scale ranging from 1 to 5, with 1 being "almost never" and 5 being "almost always." The strength of this scale is that it picks up better than most the concept of common humanity connection.[4]

- **The Compassion Scale (CS-M)** is unrelated to

the Pommier-created compassion scale (CS-P) and differs in several respects. This scale has only ten items associated with it. It uses a 1-to-7 scale, with 1 meaning "none" and 7 meaning "all." It covers the five domains of compassion (hospitality, generosity, objectivity, tolerance across social networks, and sensitivity) and measures aspects of compassion that have been proven to be enhanced through training.[5][6][7]

- **The Schwartz Center Compassionate Care scale (SCCCS)** was created to measure ratings of compassionate care from physicians during an inpatient hospital stay. Twelve items were rated from 1 to 10, with 1 being "not compassionate" and 10 being "highly compassionate" or "highly successful."[8] The downfall of the scale is that it includes a few items not related to showing compassion, such as getting results from tests promptly and whether or not the physician spent enough time with them.[9]

- **The Compassionate Care Assessment Tool (CCAT)** focuses on nursing care. The scale has patients rate the importance of each item on the list and the degree that they received this quality from the nursing caregiver. This rating scale is 1 to 4, with 1 being a poor score and 4 being excellent. One significant shortcoming of this scale is that it focuses heavily on meeting spiritual needs, which diminishes the relevance of the test with patients who are not particularly spiritual.[10][11]

- **The Relational Compassion Scale (RCS)** includes sixteen items rated on a four-point scale from 1 (do not agree) to 4 (agree strongly). This particular scale has many factors with subscales, encompassing compassion for others, self-compassion, beliefs about the compassionate levels of other people in relationship to each other, and how compassionate other people are to the individual taking the assessment.[12] The scale is intended for "relational" compassion. The relational compassion scale measures *beliefs* about how compassionate other people are to each other, and beliefs or how one feels about the degree of compassion other people have to them.

- **The Sussex-Oxford Compassion for Others Scale (SOCS-O)** is a twenty-item questionnaire that uses the five dimensions of compassion, which are often referred to in research when discussing and attempting to define compassion.[13]

- **Sussex-Oxford Compassion for the Self Scale (SOCS-S)** is also a twenty-item questionnaire that evaluates the five dimensions of compassion as related to self.[14]

It can be fun to see where we have grown with a number—especially for those of us who love data! However, these assessments are tools; while they can measure your current level of compassion, they in no way should be used as a determinant of your *capacity* for compassion. Compassion is your natural state. Our capacity to access compassion may be diminished, but compassion is always waiting to be uncovered.

Chapter Nine

INCORPORATING SELF-COMPASSION INTO YOUR DAILY LIFE

*"You've been criticizing yourself for years,
and it hasn't worked. Try approving of yourself
and see what happens."*

– Louise Hay

IN MY EARLY thirties, I had a long commute to my job in an emergency department in a neighboring town. I loved this ER (and still do to this day). Working there gave me one of the most phenomenal learning experiences I have ever had in my life.

One of the physicians there was Buddhist. Each time I worked with him I knew it was going to be a great day, because no matter what happened, he showed an incredible ability to accept things as they were. Though I didn't recognize it for what it was at the time, he had perfected *equanimity*.

My commute to this ER took me through California's wine country. It was gorgeous and so serene. I got into the habit of listening to audiobooks over and over again during my hours of driving. This time gave me solace and I learned to lean into the habit of opening up regularly to new information that helped me get grounded and find peace. In particular, I loved watching the sun rise as I drove home after a long weekend of work. My mind was a bit "soft" at these times—a perfect state for accepting new ideas and not automatically rejecting them.

Pema Chödrön was my go-to. I listened to many of her books, but my favorite was *The Places That Scare You*. There was so much that scared me at that point in my life—but thanks in part to those long drives with Pema, that began to change. Little by little, I started inching toward the things that made me uncomfortable rather than running away from them. If I could get just 3 percent closer to my truth, I told myself, that was still 3 percent closer than I was the day before.

In the years since, I've learned that it really is the small incremental changes over time that create self-compassion and lessens the fear associated with softening. Remember, we are not going for perfection; we are going for progress. If you can make a tiny amount of progress every day, you will soon experience your life in a vastly different way, and begin to reap the benefits of compassion in your physical and mental health. I know I have.

Remember, this is a journey—a lifelong journey of intentions and courageous risks to be brave, open up, be present for what is, and get closer to our own true nature.

Circling Back Around

I'll say it again: learning self-compassion isn't a hill you climb once or a task you check off a list. It's a lifelong practice. Compassion, awareness, love, forgiveness, and grace are all interwoven into a beautiful patchwork that is already residing within you.

It's important to recognize when we start any self-compassion practice that it might not go very well at first—and that, as a result, we may feel inclined to beat ourselves up for not doing it well enough, fast enough, or effectively enough. That's okay. Over time, we will develop a greater awareness of when we're doing it instead of just blindly running through our lives having unrealistic expectations of ourselves and ingesting our own poison.

In this chapter, I'll share some exercises to help you cultivate compassion and self-compassion on a daily basis. However, before we go there, I want to return to some of the key truths about compassion we explored at the beginning of this book.

Despite its power, compassion is not a magic recipe to make our lives stress-free. Nor will it empower you to feel unconditional love for everyone you meet, all the time.

That's not realistic, and it shouldn't be a goal.

Even with self-compassion, life will continue to bring its difficulties, its tragedies, and its joys. It will retain its repetitive nature—with beginning, middles, and ends all overlapping upon one another in different areas of our lives. I have found a sweetness in the simple awareness that we all suffer, we all grieve, we all love, and we all want to be loved in return. Knowing this softens the hardest places within me. We are human and imperfect, and that is beautiful in and of itself. Our common humanity is one of the things that can elicit a state of compassion—knowing that we all strive for happiness, health, and peace for ourselves and those we love. As long as we know that, it is not only okay to lack compassion or self-compassion at times, it is expected and normal.

There will always be triggers, things that we find unacceptable, and things that rock us to our core and make it appear impossible for a fountain of compassion to bubble up within us. When you begin your own journey to investigate compassion as it is, it will change you in the most beautiful way. There are still times in my life when I'm not able to meditate, and I'm not able to find the compassion I so desperately seek. Sometimes, this disappoints me. Sometimes, it disappoints the people around me. It's in these moments when I need my self-compassion the most.

Finally, the word *compass* is literally in the word compassion. I don't believe that that's a mistake. In just the same way a compass will find your physical true north, compassion can help you to find your heart's true north. Even if it can't magically take away your pain, frustration, or anger, compassion will show you where to go from here.

Compassion as a Practice

Throughout this book, we've looked in depth at what compassion and self-compassion are, how to train and measure them, and how they can affect your health and well-being. We dove into the foundational work that supports a compassionate way of being. But how, exactly, do you practice compassion and self-compassion in your everyday life?

Before we dive into instructions and techniques, it's important to acknowledge that there are many ways to find self-compassion and compassion for others. Some will work for you; others won't. Keep looking until you find practices that you can stick with. This is key, because repetition of helpful practices will get you out of the state of autonomic overwhelm so you can fully embrace what compassion has to offer. This takes time. It also takes forgiveness, love, and—you guessed it—self-compassion.

I like to think of this as "training your inner puppy."

On one of my long commutes through wine country on my way to an ER shift, I was listening to a lecture by Pema Chödrön where she said something like this: "*When you are meditating, it is essential to learn to stay, like you are training a rambunctious puppy.*"

At that time, of course, I did not know much about meditation, and I was nowhere near ready to sit with my pain (as my experience at the silent meditation retreat soon proved). But I knew how to train puppies, and I knew I felt like an untrained puppy in my life, so the analogy stuck.

You train a puppy with kindness and repetition. You never tell the dog how stupid they are; you do not hit them or punish them. If you train them with love, you will have a loyal and trusted companion. The same is true for your brain. When you undertake daily "compassion training," you train your brain to be loving and kind to yourself first; then, you'll develop the ability to radiate that intention outward.

Imagine if your brain was a trusted friend and not a mortal enemy (or worse, a sneaky trickster). It's possible with compassion.

LOVING-KINDNESS MEDITATION

As you know, I love meditation as a tool to cultivate greater compassion and self-compassion. Meditation helps us get closer to our life as it is—in our pain, and in our joy.

There are many types of meditation directly linked to self-compassion. In my opinion, the most accessible are loving-kindness meditations.

The loving-kindness meditation I share on the next page is also called *Metta* (in Pali) or *Maitri* (in Sanskrit). "Maitri" is a Sanskrit word that roughly translates to "unconditional friendship with oneself." If that doesn't scream self-compassion, I don't know what does.

The process of Maitri gives you an internal path to making friends with all the parts of yourself. Instead of looking to external sources for self-kindness and self-love, this practice helps you go within. It allows you to feel at home in your own body. There is an assumption in Maitri that there will always be suffering in human life, and being able to sit with the suffering without judgment or fear can soften the edges of it enough to make it more tolerable. It does not get rid of anything; it simply helps us not to run away from our lives and ourselves.

There are many ways of saying the following, but the following is the Metta prayer that I learned.

A Metta Prayer

May all beings be safe.
May all beings be healthy.
May all beings be happy.
May all beings live with ease.
May I be safe.
May I be healthy.
May I be happy.
May I live with ease.

To practice this meditation, sit in a quiet place and repeat the above as many times as you wish. You can close your eyes, or keep them open. You can also repeat specific phrases that elicit a sense of kindness and love within you.

If you want to express loving thoughts for a specific person, instead of saying, "All beings be safe," say their name: "May [Name] be safe. May [Name] be healthy ..."

I believe this prayer is more approachable than traditional sitting meditation because the wishes are for goodness, and also because speaking the prayer aloud helps keep your mind from wandering. Practice this for thirty days in a row and see how your brain and body change as a result!

TONGLEN MEDITATION

The word *Tonglen* loosely translates to "giving and taking."

A pilot study done in 2012 showed a significant increase in self-compassion in subjects who practiced Tonglen for eighteen minutes every other day, as measured by Neff's self-compassion questionnaire.[1] It appears from this pilot that the benefits may extend beyond the good wishes we send by augmenting our ability to stay with what is— which is critical for compassion.

Tonglen is more complex than the Maitri practice for cultivating compassion and self-compassion. In the loving-kindness Maitri meditation, no specific suffering is addressed. In Tonglen, typically, a specific issue is brought to mind—although that issue can be as general as "struggle." In Maitri practices, you do not get intimate with your suffering; in Tonglen, you will.

Breath is also central feature to the Tonglen practice,

as we use breath to bring closer the energy of suffering as well as sending the compassionate healing.

I usually direct people to start with Maitri and then go to Tonglen. I often joke that Tonglen is NLS (next level shit).

I often do a guided practice with the groups I teach; the following are the words I use to guide them through the process of giving and taking. This script is an amalgamation of many different Tonglen teachings I have experienced. I have cherry-picked what has given me the most relief from suffering, and also what has given me a feeling of bravery and the right tools to meet suffering well-equipped.

A Sample Tonglen Meditation

Think of someone who is suffering (this can be another person you love dearly, or yourself).
Consider their emotional struggle and pain, try to really be in their shoes with their struggle.
Now imagine them in front of you.
Visualize their pain as a dark cloud of thick black smoke residing in their chest.
Imagine now the celebration of joy when their pain disappears as you bring forth the end of their suffering.
Really imagine your powerful, brave, and true compassionate state of being.
Take a deep slow breath in and see the black

cloud of smoke coming closer to you.

Continue to take low and slow breaths until the black cloud is near your face. Look at this cloud and notice it has no real power; it is an illusion.

Begin to see into your chest a bright light glowing from within, strong and true and brave. Your fear dissipates and your strength rises up through this bright light of healing energy. Your true nature is arising and becoming stronger.

When you are ready, take a breath and allow the black smoke to approach your inner light . As it travels closer to your light, their suffering becomes weaker and weaker. The space for the suffering to exist becomes expansive, while the suffering itself becomes less heavy and visible.

When the black smoke finally reaches your expansive inner light, it fades into nothing, completely destroyed. Like a phoenix in the process of transmutation, the light of your true nature becomes brighter and more powerful for the transition from dark to light. From the mystery of suffering to the knowing of peace.

As you continue to breathe out, the suffering is completely eliminated. In your out breath, you send love, peace, and joy, The suffering never touches you. Your inner light dissolves and transforms the pain; you are divinely protected. As you exhale, the light travels (never leaving you) but growing and

expanding to the person (or people) who were suf-
fering giving them everything they need. They are
peaceful, happy, healthy, and vibrant. You see the
light that is within you begin to grow within them
and their suffering ends.

Come back to yourself and thank your inner
light and true nature for showing up for this
healing.

Rest in this.

Practically speaking, this is what is happening with Tonglen. As you inhale, you take in the difficulty of the struggle, feeling it as deeply as you can, and your compassionate inward light transforms it. As you exhale, you send and give more space/light to the self/other person/ population/issue. With each breath, you create the expansion of heart and mind that is needed to carry the weight of the suffering that exists.

This is no small order, and the practice can be difficult, especially when you are new to it. Be gentle with yourself, and stop if it feels like too much. Go as small as you need to; I have done Tonglen with the struggle of an ant carrying a twig ten times its size. You can also go as big as you want when you are ready, as Mother Earth is always looking for some healing.

It's important to note that the purpose of Tonglen practice is not to get rid of all suffering in the world. That is impossible. Life is full of suffering. Tonglen simply allows us to make more space and transform what we can with a peaceful, grounded place for the suffering to land so that we may process it and move forward. This gives us, and the object(s) of our meditation, more ease in carrying the human experience of suffering. The effort that Tonglen takes can create great releases of pain and suffering. This practice does not require you to "take on" another's suffering; rather, it uses the struggle as the cure, and the poison as medicine. It's beautiful.

SIX IDEAS TO CULTIVATE COMPASSION

I've mentioned Kristen Neff several times throughout this book, and with good reason. Her work on self-compassion has long been an inspiration for my practice and my research.

The following six ideas for practicing self-compassion in everyday settings are adapted from Kristen Neff's book, *Self-Compassion: Stop Beating Yourself Up and Leave Insecurity Behind*.[2] The following are ideas mentioned in her book that I have found to be helpful, along with additional activities that I've woven into my personal practice.

Idea #1: How Would You Treat a Friend?

When patients in the clinic are having a health issue or psychological obstacle that they are trying to overcome and heal, they are often very hard on themselves. I ask them, "If this were happening to your best friend, what advice or words of comfort would you give them?"

Then, when they share those words, I ask, "Is that what you're saying to yourself right now?" Invariably, the answer is no.

So, ask yourself, "If my best friend told me they were experiencing what I'm going through now, how would I view the situation? How would I respond? Would I treat them the same way I'm treating myself?" The answer will guide you toward greater self-compassion.

Idea #2: A Self-Compassion Break

This exercise is wonderful because it can be done quickly and to great effect.

During your day, find a quiet place where you will be undisturbed for five minutes or so. Bring up a event that was difficult for you, and say a statement to yourself that acknowledges your struggle and suffering .Be present as you say these things out loud or to yourself.

Here are some suggestions:

- "This is really difficult, and I am capable."
- "This hurts. I can hold this hurt with care."
- "I am confused/scared/worried, and that's okay."
- "I will give myself (or another) the grace to be imperfect in this situation."
- "Suffering is a part of life, and of being human. I am not alone in suffering. Everyone

suffers, and right now I am suffering."

- "May I be supportive and kind to myself through this suffering."

- "May I soon be well and happy and free from suffering."

Breathe into this patience and acceptance of your own humanity and suffering knowing you are creating a soft place to land for yourself. (Bonus: these statements can also be used to help someone else who is suffering).

Idea #3: Self-Compassion Journaling

Many compassion classes and books recommend a journaling practice as a conduit to self-compassion. I love the following methods in particular because it gives voice to all the parts of me: the wounded and the healed, the brave and the fearful, the confused and the clear.

To begin, get out a notebook and a pen and find your best place to write. For some, it's a busy bus station; for others, it's a desk in a room with a lock and a key. You will know you've found your place when you feel safe to write anything.

In this practice, you will write a list of your ongoing frustrations: the struggles you have, current situations you find demanding, or something that recently has made you feel inadequate or imperfect. Write down how you have been responding to the situation.

Then, write a response to the above like that you might expect to hear from a supportive, kind, and loving friend.

(This "friend" can be real or imagined. Sometimes, I write my responses in the voice of Morgan Freeman or Glenda the good witch.)

Be specific about the inadequacies and imperfections you felt in the first part, and respond to each issue one by one with love and kindness in the voice of your supportive friend.

Finally, I recommend that you pause and really feel what you've written—both the initial part and the loving response. This step is critical to allow that loving response to penetrate deeply enough to elicit a felt sense of self-compassion and a feeling of care from within.

With repetition, this exercise can be a guidepost to return to when our self-compassion runs low.

You can also use a variation of the above practice on a daily basis to grow your innate self-compassion.

To do this, begin by writing about the events of the day and how they made you feel. Were there situations or conversations that caused you to feel insecure, or that caused your inner critic to judge you harshly? Sum these up in a few sentences.

When you're done, rewrite your account of the day to be kinder and more loving.

For example: Imagine you went to the grocery store but forgot your wallet at home. Perhaps your self-talk was harsh. *"You idiot! If you could only get your shit together, this kind of thing wouldn't happen!"* Write down what your inner critic said.

Then, bring up the more compassionate part of yourself. Notice that these kinds of things happen to lots of people all the time, and it doesn't make *them* idiots. However, it does make them forgetful, and perhaps indicates that they're trying to do too much. In this way, taking time to slow down doesn't make somebody an idiot; in fact, it could make them quite brilliant and increase their ability to take care of themselves! More pragmatically, you can look for evidence that you are not alone. I mean, why would Apple make key ring finders if people did not lose their keys? It happens so frequently that Apple is profiting from it!

Speaking to yourself with kindness at this point could look like this: "It's okay that I forgot my keys. Everybody forgets things sometimes. It's not the end of the world."

In this process, it is crucial to determine what we really want. If we lose sight of our goal, we can go down less helpful roads—particularly because self-criticism can serve as a way to motivate ourselves. When we notice ourselves using this method of motivation, knowing what we are trying to accomplish can invite a more pragmatic and compassionate way to motivate ourselves. This will take practice—but remember that encouraging with fear is not as effective as motivating with love, kindness, and compassion.

Journaling can also be used to remind yourself of the compassionate aspects of your day. Maybe you had a moment (or more than one) that was particularly good. Maybe you witnessed or were part of a compassionate act. If so, write down what it was and how it made you feel.

Try to tease out how your body felt, and how the interaction steered your day in a positive direction. Dissect how it came to be and uncover the goodness within.

This daily practice is wonderful because it draws on our innate compassion and not that of an external voice or force (like my beloved Morgan Freeman). In addition, it can help us to gain emotional perspective and distance from the events of the day.

Maybe, one day, we'll forget how to criticize yourself (and others), and we'll just write love notes. This is my wish for you, and for me.

Idea #4: Supportive Touch

Supportive touch can be challenging, particularly for those with a traumatic history. Please use care and discretion.

If it feels good to you, place your hand over your heart and take a couple of deep, slow breaths, acknowledging the humanness of your heartbeat and your sense of touch. Some feel more comforted by putting a hand on their belly, placing their hands on their cheeks, or simply cupping their hands in their lap. Experiment to see what feels comforting to you. Stay with this feeling of comfort until you gain a sense of love and gratitude for the body you are in.

One of my favorite ways to use this is to simply wrap my arms around myself and gently rub my elbows. It's a very low-key way to give myself a gentle reminder that it's all okay, I am okay and safe.

When I have more space and time, I use a technique called Emotional Freedom Technique (EFT). This is not part of Dr Neff's instruction, but is a personal favorite of mine. It find that it is a beautiful way to increase awareness and ground my body as I begin "tapping into" my true nature of compassion. Studies have shown EFT to be a valuable tool to alleviate multiple different health markers as well as decrease pain, anxiety and depression.[3]

These physical aspects of compassion are very good at releasing oxytocin, a bonding and feel-good hormone. This process can help change your biochemistry, allowing for this to be a more well-traveled pathway in your body and brain, and making it easier each time you practice.

Idea #5: Dealing with Critical Self-Talk

This is another on-the-spot tool that can be used when you are out and about during your day.

It can often be challenging to notice when we are communicating with ourselves in a negative way, but this awareness gets easier with practice. My own inner critic has repeating themes, and those patterns can be recognized with ease when I use this practice on a regular basis.

So, let's use our powers of rumination for compassion, not harm! In moments when you are feeling frustrated and disappointed, or being unkind to yourself, try to remember what you've just said to yourself in your mind. Was it self-critical or harsh? Once you notice what your inner voice (or inner critic) is actually saying, you can approach it with compassion.

One way to know if you are having an inner-critic moment is to tune in to what your body is feeling. If it is tense or stressed, dig a little deeper into your thoughts and see if there is a link.

Speak to this inner critic in your mind, or out loud if you can. Use the tone and language you would use with a young child who is acting out and needs some extra support. (That is basically what an inner critic is: a primal, emotional, immature part of ourselves, or the voice of someone who was not kind to us in our past.)

Instead of punishing or pushing back against the voice in your head with more criticism, try kindness. You can say things like, "I know it's tough for you to be quiet, but I need you to take a little time-out and rest." Or, "I appreciate you trying to protect me from harm, embarrassment, and vulnerability. Those aspects of being human can be scary."

Ask your inner critic if it's okay for your more compassionate self to speak a few words. (This is another great time to call on your compassionate, supportive "friend" to help counter the criticisms and judgments from that harsh part of your mind.)

When I'm flailing in the deep sea of self-flagellation, I often use this simple statement: "Hey there, Catherine. You are really struggling right now. Here's some love." It amazes me that, when I send myself that little bit of love, it immediately calms me and creates space for something more aligned with who I really am.

A more lighthearted method I use is to give my inner

critic a crazy voice. Sometimes I'll use Goofy or Kermit the Frog. When I hear those two talking in my head, the ridiculousness is disarming, and interrupts my critic's tirade. I am then ready to smile and bring some levity to an otherwise negative situation.

Idea 6: Caring for the Caregiver

Often, those in caregiving positions struggle most with self-compassion. It is crucial to take care of yourself when you are in a caregiving position. This does not mean only when you are working as a professional caregiver, but also times in your life when you are caring for a loved one, a pet, a friend, or even caretaking a plot of land.

"Caring for the caregiver" will look different for every person. Sometimes it can be just giving yourself a few quiet moments alone between the chaotic moments. For me, it's allowing myself the freedom to watch a Christmas movie in July or turn on some early '80s soul music and really let it rip. I used to be afraid to use the full range of my voice and body to sing and move, so it took me some practice to feel freer in my own skin. It was worth every second. I still struggle doing this in front of people, but there are a few people with whom I can do this. (It is crazy funny. You know who you are.)

Do not be discouraged if it feels a bit unnatural at first. Try some of these suggestions and see what works for you. Whatever you choose, make sure to do it regularly and with great compassion.

***

You do not have to use Dr. Neff's ideas for compassionate daily living all at once, or even incorporate all of them into your practice over time. Try a few and see how you feel. Think of it as a scientific experiment and start with curiosity. You may be surprised what brings you back to your most compassionate self.

My Personal Favorite Conduits to Compassion

My favorite compassion practices are simple. I'll share some of them with you here.

GARDENING

Gardening is not an intuitive way to compassion. However, I promise that gardening will open you up to many facets of life. We discover through gardening that even the simplest plant needs good soil (food), ample water, and sunshine to survive. The plants we care for tend to do better and thrive, just like our relationships and our own bodies. You'll be surprised that, even with a fairly significant level of neglect, most things will thrive; this might give you hope for those times when your circumstances may not be optimal. Sometimes I forget where I planted a few things, yet they pop up again every spring, little reminders of my past hard work rewarding me in the present with beauty.

Gardening also gives us lessons on how to deal with death and impermanence with compassion and grace. For example, I killed not one but *two* cherry trees in my backyard. I did everything right, and yet, no go. Then, I planted a nectarine tree, and it is flourishing. Lessons on forced growth, right place, and right timing are plentiful in a garden.

CRYING

Crying with and for myself is sometimes the best act of self-compassion. Crying has gotten such a bad rap. As we discovered in our discussion on immune function, crying has antibacterial and antiviral qualities. It also allows us to acknowledge the pain of being human and is part of our common humanity. How do we know a newborn is okay? They cry. The same is true of an adult.

Sometimes we need help to have a good cry. Music can help. A few of my favorite "cry songs" are "Vocalise" by Rachmaninoff, "Why" by Annie Lennox, "Both Sides Now" by Joni Mitchell, "Just Breathe" by Pearl Jam, and "Hallelujah" by Leonard Cohen.

Music is a conduit to compassion because it makes us *feel*. It helps us to move and be present in the now. Or, it can take us to another time and place entirely, and liberate the stagnant emotions of our past. Whenever I hear Billy Squier's "She's a Runner," I can almost feel my fourteen-year-old self hanging out at Cal Skate on a Friday night. I feel free—and I also feel all of her angst and teen trouble. I send her compassion—and, like a boomerang, it comes back to fifty-three-year-old me. Magic.

SLOWING DOWN

Slowing down in our busy lives is an act of compassion.

For most high achievers, our achievements come at a cost. We can run ourselves into the ground if we don't take a pause. Sometimes, it's only for a minute or two. Sometimes, it's for a month. Sometimes, it's for a year or more. There is a season for everything; slowing down is part of nature. Have you ever looked at a tree and said to it, "You are not blooming fast enough"? Of course not. We accept nature's seasons and imperfections with a sense of awe. Let's do the same with our own seasons.

COMPASSIONATE BATHS

This is one of my favorites. I learned this particular way of bathing from the movie *What the Bleep Do We Know!?* It may seem a bit wild to you, but give it a chance.

I take a bath with children's bath crayons. I draw little hearts over my body with the words "I love you." This is an intense and deliberate way to communicate love to myself. I'll admit, it felt weird at first, but now when I need a very deep treatment of compassionate love for myself (especially as I age and my body changes), this is my go-to. I also add oils whose scents bring me joy: lavender and tuberose are particularly blissful for me. This is compassion in action for me when I am weary.

THE SWEETEST PARTS OF ME

There are actually two practices in this category, and they are as follows:

Photographs

In this practice, I take out a photo of myself as a young child as a reminder of my inner goodness, innocence, and sweetness, and put that photo in a place I will see it often. I move it around every three weeks to another location where I will continue to see and notice it, and not forget about it. When I become harsh with myself, I know it's time for me to look at that photo. I go over to the photo and ask myself, "Self, would you say those words to this child?" If the answer is no (spoiler alert, it's *always* no) I apologize and speak words that are brave, true, compassionate, and kind to my photo and to me.

When I first started this practice, it would always end in tears. I think over time I have become a better friend to this little girl; after all she is me, and I am her. As time has gone on, it has become a wonderfully sweet practice.

If you don't have a photo of yourself as a child, a photo of any child can work. Even just seeing a child being a child can help you focus your intention for compassion.

Anchoring Memories

Even with all the chaos and uncertainty of my childhood, I have some pretty amazing memories to draw on. These moments of innocence and purity can be a lifeline to compassion; remembering them can be both a foundation of compassion and a practice in and of itself. Your body will recall peaceful experiences in the same visceral way it recalls trauma. So, bring the peaceful moments with you into your current life.

When I was a child, we had a bing cherry tree in our backyard. I'd climb up the tree, rest between the branches, and read or write all day. In March and April, I'd sit among the blossoms, and in May, I'd be alongside the cherries. Even in the winter, without the green leaves, I felt peaceful, safe, and inspired in that tree. In its arms, I was able to be with whatever was going on without knowing that was what I was doing.

Remembering those moments now, I send compassion to my past self—and, from the past, I can send compassion to the me who exists today through the eyes of my own innocence. It can be a profound practice.

Try to recall where you felt safe as a child. Really embody it as best you can. When you are safe and secure, where do you feel it? Anchor to that. How can you bring that into your daily life?

It is much easier to be kind and compassionate with ourselves and others when we are in a place that evokes those types of emotions. As an adult, I will still climb a tree now and again—although I do have to pick them a bit more carefully—but even from the ground, trees feel like sacred spaces to me. In my current backyard, there is a large sycamore tree. When I first met my husband, who is a pilot, he would often fly over my house at a set time. I would lie there in my hammock and watch his plane from between the branches of the tree. I could feel his presence hundreds or thousands of feet above me; ironically, I felt grounded and peaceful watching him fly overhead.

In this same tree, I now have a treehouse. Originally built for my son, it now serves as my getaway. I climb up the ladder, sit in my chair, and reconnect with my innocence, my joy, and my peace

You have a place that reminds you of freedom, groundedness, and compassion, too. Find your place, and go there often.

Compassion Training

When you are ready for a more formal and structured practice of compassion, there are many ways to go. While I do not believe that any one way is the right way, I do know that, if you search, you will find a right way for you. Here are a few of my suggestions for a formal education in compassion:

- **The Compassion Project** is free online and geared to younger school-age children. That being said, the fundamentals of this program are for everyone.[4]

- **Cognitive-Based Compassion Training (CBCT)** was initially developed to aid undergraduate university students in increasing their emotional resilience.[5] There are many places to take this course, usually through universities. Different formats (virtual and in person) are available. This is a great option if you want to dive deeper as a layperson or become a certified trainer and give the gift to compassion to others. This program in particular has been studied and found to be beneficial for at-risk foster children.[6]

- **Compassion-Focused Therapy (CFT)** is practiced by many therapists; Paul Gilbert is credited with its development.[7][8] This type of therapy can be particularly helpful with distracted behaviors (or what is sometimes called a "tricky" brain). I don't know about you, but I can honestly say that my brain can be very tricky at times. CFT can help with this.

- **The Compassion Cultivation Training (CCT)** program developed at Stanford University is an eight-week program developed for caregivers, physicians, and psychologists. This program has been studied demonstrating greater levels of compassion to the individuals who attend.[9]

- **The Center for Compassion and Altruism Research and Education (CCARE)** at Stanford University has a year-long program to take a deep dive into your inner world and compassion. In this program, you develop a plan for creating more compassion in the world using your individual gifts and talents. It's well worth the investment of time and energy if you are committed to a compassionate path.[10]

Living Compassionately

You can try any or all the practices in this chapter to increase your self-compassion—or something else entirely! Just pick a practice that makes sense to you and try it. If it doesn't work, try another until you find one that helps.

Here is a short list of other suggestions to explore:

- Kundalini yoga
- Tai Chi
- Qi Gong
- Bodywork (massage, Reiki, acupuncture, Bowen Therapy)
- Getting support (aka, hiring people to do the jobs that you feel bad about not doing).

Also, know that your methods may change over time. That's okay! What works on Monday may not work on

Tuesday. Given the amount of suffering we encounter on a daily basis—particularly working with patients in health-care settings—we have a deep, abiding need for this type of healing. Holding on to our suffering can become too much, and these practices give us a way not only to manage the stress, but to transform it into a healing practice.

No matter what path you are guided toward, keep working at it, because the benefits outweigh the effort many times over. The more you practice, the easier it will be. Your brain loves repetition. In fact, your brain loves it so much that when you do something repeatedly, your brain makes pathways to make the process of what you do, think, or feel more efficient. The more compassionate acts you practice, the easier it becomes over time—so be careful, or you might just change your mind.

Conclusion

IN MARCH OF 2023, I attended a compassion immersion retreat led by two of my teachers from Stanford University, Neelama Eyres and Robert Cusick.

I set an intention for this weekend-long experience to deepen my heart connection to compassion and ease up a bit on my intellectualization of compassion. This program was an opportunity to dive deep into the applications of compassion, and I was very excited to be included.

As we were readying ourselves for meditation, Robert eloquently spoke of anchors and their use. But then, he said something that was so curious to me. He said we could use our longing to come home as an anchor.

If you have ever had this longing—the longing for "home" that is so much deeper than the physical—you will understand how profound this instruction was. When I heard Robert's words, I had the biggest hot flash of my life. Every cell in my body was on fire. I wondered how the hell he knew that I had always felt this longing to "go home" that had nothing to do with my childhood home or any place I'd ever lived. I had never heard of anyone speak of this longing in this way—as something to follow, rather than dismiss. I felt like Robert had just presented me with the Holy Grail, the one artifact that contained all the most confused and lost bits of myself.

Robert explained that using this anchor of longing to go home can, in time, lead us *home to ourselves.* My head almost exploded. *Are you kidding me?* I thought. *Could it really be that simple?* I didn't want to *go* home, I wanted to *come* home. To me.

I *missed* me. I *longed for* me.

The moment I realized this, I felt a peace and connectedness that I had never felt before. As of this writing, the journey to return home to myself has begun.

This compassionate act of returning to oneself has the possibility of taming the most reactive of personalities. After reading this book, you have a better understanding of the psychophysiology of compassion. You may even be inspired to use the tools and knowledge herein to return closer to your natural state of compassion and well-being. I hope you are able to integrate this information and practices into your daily life to the benefit of all those you encounter.

My greatest hope is that this book helps you to come home to yourself in the way writing it did for me.

As I'm sure you noticed, I shared a number of highly personal stories in this book. I didn't do this to air out my dirty laundry, but rather to show that my understanding of compassion is not merely theoretical, and it did not come lightly. I struggled. I bled. I healed. And I still struggle, bleed, and heal—only now, I do it with more grace, love, and compassion for my humanness.

I acknowledge that this is hard work. I also know it can be effortless with practice. I have felt both (in rapid succession at times), and I know those two seemingly oppositional statements are not in opposition at all. This is life. Equanimity is the art of holding the struggle as if it is just as precious as the ease. Compassion makes room for all of it.

The pandemic brought to the surface all the underlying pathology within our medical system and our society at large. It is my intention that this book presents us with an opportunity to begin to heal it—but first, we have to name it. We must acknowledge that we have been traumatized, and that our nervous systems are paying the price. When our nervous systems have gone on high alert for too long, we become fatigued, frightened, and angry, and we burn the fuck out.

I believe—I *know*, with my whole being—that compassion and self-compassion will help us heal. These may not be the only solutions we need, but compassion for ourselves and others is certainly the single most important quality that we can bring forth to enable healing in a way that honors what we've been through, who we are, and where we are going. Without these qualities, we are sunk.

We need to bring this state of self-compassion to the forefront of the way we practice medicine and the way we live our lives. We need compassion to be the number-one quality of our leaders and administration in every single hospital. We've become too focused on the bottom line, throughput, and changing workflows every single day. These things may be necessary, but they should not be our top priority when lives are on the line. Our lives.

We need our hospitals and clinics to be safe, compassionate places. We cannot provide a place of healing for our patients (or ourselves) if we're perpetually operating in a state of flight, fight, freeze, or fawning. If we continue the way we are, we will burn out and burn down like a dry Christmas tree in January.

This is not a change we can bring about in our medical system, our society at large, or even ourselves, overnight. Nor can we do it with a few grand gestures or sweeping changes. These types of actions rarely last beyond the honeymoon phase. This will be a long, slow process that will require dedication and commitment from individuals at a level on par with our original medical schooling.

The public health officer in me says: *Slow, incremental changes over time: that is how we make lasting change. However slow, it is imperative that we begin.*

It's my hope that this book will inspire you to join me on this path. As you now know, compassion is not for the weak of heart, mind, or spirit. Compassion is rugged badassery. This is where we find warriors and wounded alike, often within the same person. Together, with one simple act of compassion at a time, we will change everything about how we live, work, and heal.

Start anywhere you can. Start small. Start big. Start over, and over, and over again if you must. I know I have had to. Start today, just as you are. I promise you; it will be the most fiercely strong and tender thing you do in this lifetime.

May peace, grace, and compassion not only follow you throughout the days of your life, but may it also spring forth from them.

With Compassion,
Catherine W. Schweikert, PhD

Endnotes

CHAPTER ONE

(1).   Gu, J; Cavanagh, K; Baer, R; Strauss, C. "An empirical examination of the factor structure of compassion." *PLoS ONE*, 2017; 12(2). DOI: 10.1371/journal.pone.0172471

(2).   Kanov, J M; Maitlis, S; Worline, M C; Dutton, J E; Frost, P J; Lilius, J M. "Compassion in Organizational Life." *American Behavioral Scientist*, 2004; 47(6), 808-827. DOI: 10.1177/0002764203260211

(3).   Sommers-Spijkerman, M; Elfrink, T R; Drossaert, C H C; Schreurs, K M G; Bohlmeijer, E T. "Exploring compassionate attributes and skills among individuals participating in compassion-focused therapy for enhancing well-being." *Psychology and Psychotherapy*, 2020; 93(3), 555-571. DOI: 10.1111/papt.12235

(4).   Pommier, E; Neff, K D; Tóth-Király, I. "The Development and Validation of the Compassion Scale." *Assessment*, 2020; 27(1), 21-39. DOI: 10.1177/1073191119874108

CHAPTER TWO

(1).   Breines, J G; Chen, S. "Self-compassion increases self-improvement motivation." *Personality & Social Psychology Bulletin*, 2012; 38(9), 1133-1143. DOI:10.1177/0146167212445599

(2).   Ronningstrom, E. "Narcissistic personality disorder: Facing DSM-V." *Psychiatric Annals*, 2009; 39(3), 111-121. https://sakkyndig.com/psykologi/artvit/ronningstam2009.pdf

(3).   Bluth, K; Campo, R A; Futch, W S; Gaylord, S A. "Age and gender differences in the associations of self-compassion and emotional well-being in a large adolescent sample." *Journal of Youth and Adolescence*, 2017; 46(4), 840-853. DOI:10.1007/s10964-016-0567-2

CHAPTER THREE

(1).   Saarinen, A I L; Keltikangas-Järvinen, L; Hintsa, T; Pulkki-Råback, L; Ravaja, N; Lehtimäki, T; Raitakari, O; Hintsanen, M. "Does Compassion Predict Blood Pressure and Hypertension? The Modifying Role of Familial Risk for Hypertension." *International Journal of Behavioral Medicine*, 2020; 27(5), 527-538. DOI: 10.1007/s12529-020-09886-5

(2).   Thurston, R C; Fritz, M M; Chang, Y; Barinas Mitchell, E; Maki, P M. "Self-compassion and subclinical cardiovascular disease among midlife women." *Health Psychology*, 2021; 40(11), 747-753. DOI: 10.1037/hea0001137

(3).   Kirby, J N. "Compassion interventions: The programmes, the evidence, and implications for research and practice." *Psychology and Psychotherapy*, 2017; 90(3), 432-455. DOI: 10.1111/papt.12104

(4).   Kirby, J N; Doty, J R; Petrocchi, N; Gilbert, P. "The Current and Future Role of Heart Rate Variability for Assessing and Training Compassion." *Frontiers in Public Health*, 2017; 5:40. DOI: 10.3389/fpubh.2017.0004

(5).   Svendsen, J L; Osnes, B; Binder, P; Dundas, I; Visted, E; Nordby, H; Sørensen, L. "Correction to: Trait self-compassion reflects emotional flexibility through an association with high vagally mediated heart rate variability." *Mindfulness,* 2018; 9(6), 1994-1995. DOI:10.1007/s12671-018-1007-z

(6).   Arch, J J; Brown, K W; Dean, D J; Landy, L N; Brown, K; Laudenslager, M L. "Self-compassion training modulates alpha-amylase, heart rate variability, and subjective responses to social evaluative threat in women." *Psychoneuroendocrinology,* 2014; 42, 49-58. DOI: 10.1016/j.psyneuen.2013.12.018

(7).   Arch, J J; Brown, et al., 2014.

(8).   Luo, X; Qiao, L; Che, X. "Self-compassion Modulates Heart Rate Variability and Negative Affect to Experimentally Induced Stress." *Mindfulness,* 2018; 9(2). DOI: 10.1007/s12671-018-0900-9

(9).   Tian, S; Luo, X; Che, X; Xu, G. "Self-Compassion Demonstrating a Dual Relationship with Pain Dependent on High-Frequency Heart Rate Variability." *Pain Research & Management,* 2020; 3126036-6. DOI: 10.1155/2020/3126036

(10).   Petrocchi, N; Ottaviani, C; Couyoumdjian, A. "Compassion at the mirror: Exposure to a mirror increases the efficacy of a self-compassion manipulation in enhancing soothing positive affect and heart rate variability." *Journal of Positive Psychology,* 2017; 12(6), 525-536. DOI: 10.1080/17439760.2016.1209544

(11).   Lutz, A; Greischar, L L; Perlman, D M; Davidson, R J. "BOLD signal in insula is differentially related to cardiac function during compassion meditation in experts vs. novices." *NeuroImage,* 2009; 47(3), 1038-1046. DOI: 10.1016/j.neuroimage.2009.04.081

(12).   Noh, S; Cho, H. "Psychological and Physiological Effects of the Mindful Lovingkindness Compassion Program on Highly Self-Critical University Students in South Korea." *Frontiers in Psychology,* 2020; DOI: 10.3389/fpsyg.2020.585743

CHAPTER FOUR

(1).   Weng, H Y; Fox, A S; Shackman, A J; Stodola, D E; Caldwell, J Z K; Olson, M C; Rogers, G M; Davidson, R J. "Compassion Training Alters Altruism and Neural Responses to Suffering." *Psychological Science*; 2013; 24(7), 1171-1180. DOI: 10.1177/0956797612469537

(2).   Ashar, Y K; Andrews-Hanna, J R; Halifax, J; Dimidjian, S; Wager, T D. "Effects of compassion training on brain responses to suffering others." *Social Cognitive and Affective Neuroscience,* 2021; 16(10), 1036–1047. DOI: 10.1093/scan/nsab052

(3).   Waytz, A; Zaki, J; Mitchell, J P. "Response of dorsomedial prefrontal cortex predicts altruistic behavior." The Journal of Neuroscience, 2012; 32(22), 7646-7650. DOI: 10.1523/JNEUROSCI.6193-11.2012

(4).   Dimidjian, S; Wager, T D; Ashar, Y K; Andrews-Hanna, J. "Toward a Neuroscience of Compassion." *Positive Neuroscience,* Oxford University Press, 2016. DOI: 10.1093/acprof:oso/9780199977925.003.0009

(5).   Beadle, J N; Paradiso, S; Tranel, D. "Ventromedial Prefrontal Cortex Is Critical for Helping Others Who Are Suffering." *Frontiers in Neurology,* 2018; 9, 288. DOI: 10.3389/fneur.2018.00288

(6).   Weng, H Y, et al., 2013

(7).   Smith, K S; Tindell, A J; Aldridge, J W; Berridge, K C. "Ventral pallidum roles in reward and motivation." *Behavioural Brain Research*, 2009; 196(2), 155-167. DOI: 10.1016/j.bbr.2008.09.038

(8).   Dimidjian, S, et al, 2016

(9).   Daniel, R; Pollmann, S. "A universal role of the ventral striatum in reward-based learning: Evidence from human studies." *Neurobiology of Learning and Memory,* 2014; 114, 90-100. DOI: 10.1016/j.nlm.2014.05.002

(10).   Klimecki, O M; Leiberg, S; Ricard, M; Singer, T. "Differential pattern of functional brain plasticity after compassion and empathy training." *Social Cognitive and Affective Neuroscience,* 2014; 9(6), 873-879. DOI: 10.1093/scan/nst060

(11).   Kim, J J; Parker, S L; Doty, J R; Cunnington, R; Gilbert, P; Kirby, J N. "Neurophysiological and behavioural markers of compassion." *Scientific Reports,* 2020; 10(1), 1-9. DOI: 10.1038/s41598-020-63846-3

(12). Klimecki, O M; Leiberg, S; Lamm, C; Singer, T. "Functional neural plasticity and associated changes in positive affect after compassion training." *Cerebral Cortex*, 2013; 23(7), 1552-1561. DOI: 10.1093/cercor/bhs142

(13). Watson, D; Clark, L A; Tellegen, A. "Development and validation of brief measures of positive and negative affect: the PANAS scales." *Journal of Personality and Social Psychology*, 1988; 54(6), 1063-1070. DOI: 10.1037//0022-3514.54.6.1063

(14). Klimecki, O M, et al., 2013

(15). Klimecki, O M, et al., 2013

(16). Serafini, R A; Pryce, K D; Zachariou, V. "The Mesolimbic Dopamine System in Chronic Pain and Associated *Affective Comorbidities*." Biological Psychiatry, 2020; 87(1), 64-73. DOI: 10.1016/j.biopsych.2019.10.018

(17). Bruneau, E G; Dufour, N; Saxe, R. "Social cognition in members of conflict groups: behavioural and neural responses in Arabs, Israelis and South Americans to each other's misfortunes." *Philosophical Transactions of the Royal Society B: Biological Sciences*. 2012; 367(1589), 717-730. DOI: 10.1098/rstb.2011.0293

(18). Klimecki, O M, et al., 2014

(19). Kim, J J; Cunnington, R; Kirby, J N. "The neurophysiological basis of compassion: An fMRI meta-*analysis of compassion and its related neural processes.*" *Neuroscience and Biobehavioral Reviews*, 2020; 108, 112-123. DOI: 10.1016/j. neubiorev.2019.10.023

(20). Watson, D, et al., 1988

(21). Klimecki, O M, et al., 2013

(22). Klimecki, O M, et al., 2014

(23). Singer, T; Klimecki, O M. "Empathy and compassion." *Current Biology*, 2014; 24(18), R875-R878. DOI: 10.1016/j.cub.2014.06.054

(24). Dimidjian, S, et al, 2016

(25). Kilner, J M; Lemon, R N. "What We Know Currently about Mirror Neurons." *Current Biology*, 2013; 23(23), R1057-R1062. DOI: 10.1016/j.cub.2013.10.051

(26). Lutz, A; Brefczynski-Lewis, J; Johnstone, T; Davidson, R J. "Regulation of the Neural Circuitry of Emotion by Compassion Meditation: Effects of Meditative Expertise." *PLoS ONE*, 2008; 3(3). DOI: 10.1371/journal.pone.0001897

(27). Lutz, A; Greischar, L L; Perlman, D M; Davidson, R J. "BOLD signal in insula is differentially related to cardiac function during compassion meditation in experts vs. novices." *NeuroImage*, 2009; 47(3), 1038-1046. DOI: 10.1016/j.neuroimage.2009.04.081

(28). Braboszcz, C; Cahn, B R; Levy, J; Fernandez, M; Delorme, A. "Increased Gamma Brainwave Amplitude Compared to Control in Three Different Meditation Traditions." *PLoS ONE*, 2017; 12(1). DOI: 10.1371/journal.pone.0170647

CHAPTER FIVE

(1). Porges, S W. "Orienting in a defensive world: mammalian modifications of our evolutionary heritage. A Polyvagal Theory." *Psychophysiology*, 1995; 32(4), 301-318. DOI: 10.1111/j.1469-8986.1995.tb01213.x

(2). Porges, S W. "The polyvagal perspective." *Biological Psychology*, 2007; 74(2), 116-143. DOI: 10.1016/j.biopsycho.2006.06.009

(3). Porges, S W. *The Pocket Guide to the Polyvagal Theory: The Transformative Power of Feeling Safe.* W. W. Norton & Co, 2017. https://psycnet.apa.org/record/2012-32693-000

(4). Stellar, J E; Cohen, A; Oveis, C; Keltner, D. "Affective and physiological responses to the suffering of others: compassion and vagal activity." *Journal of Personality and Social Psychology*, 2015; 108(4), 572-585. DOI: 10.1037/pspi0000010

(5). Keltner, D; Stellar, J E. *Compassion: Concepts, Research and Applications*, compiled by Gilbert, P. Routledge/Taylor & Francis Group, 2017. https://www.routledge.com/Compassion-Concepts-Research-and-Applications/Gilbert/p/book/9781138957190

(6). Di Bello, M; Carnevali, L; Petrocchi, N; Thayer, J F; Gilbert, P; Ottaviani, C. "The compassionate vagus: A meta-analysis on the connection between compassion and heart rate variability." *Neuroscience & Biobehavior Reviews,* 2020; 116:21-30. DOI: 10.1016/j.neubiorev.2020.06.016

(7). Shaltout, H A; Tooze, J A; Rosenberger, E; Kemper, K J. "Time, Touch, and Compassion: Effects on Autonomic Nervous System and Well-Being." *Explore,* 2012; 8(3), 177-184. DOI: 10.1016/j.explore.2012.02.001

(8). Esch, T.; Stefano, G B. "The neurobiological link between compassion and love." *Medical Science Monitor,* 2011; 17(3), RA65-RA75. DOI: 10.12659/MSM.881441

CHAPTER SIX

(1). Junttila, I S. "Tuning the Cytokine Responses: An Update on Interleukin (IL)-4 and IL-13 Receptor Complexes." *Frontiers in Immunology,* 2018; 9:888. DOI: 10.3389/fimmu.2018.00888

(2). Justiz Vaillant, A A; Qurie, A. "Interleukin." *StatPearls* [Internet], 2021. https://www.ncbi.nlm.nih.gov/books/NBK499840/

(3). Tanaka, T; Narazaki, M; Kishimoto, T. "IL-6 in Inflammation, Immunity, and Disease." *Cold Spring Harbor Perspectives in Biology,* 2014; 6(10), a016295. DOI: 10.1101/cshperspect.a016295

(4). Pradhan, A D; Manson, J E; Rifai, N; Buring, J E; Ridker, P M. "C-Reactive Protein, Interleukin 6, and Risk of Developing Type 2 Diabetes Mellitus." *JAMA: The Journal of the American Medical Association,* 2001; 286(3), 327-334. DOI: 10.1001/jama.286.3.327

(5). Pace, T; Negi, L T; Adame, D; Cole, S; Sivilli, T; Brown, T; Issa, M; Raison, C. "Effect of compassion meditation on autonomic, neuroendocrine and inflammatory pathway reactivity to psychosocial stress." *Psychoneuroendocrinology,* 2009; 34(1), 87–98. DOI: 10.1016/j.psyneuen.2008.08.011

(6).   Montero-Marin, J; Andrés-Rodríguez, L; Tops, M; Luciano, J
         V; Navarro-Gil, M; Feliu-Soler, A; López-del-Hoyo, Y; Garcia-
         Campayo, J. "Effects of attachment-based compassion therapy
         (ABCT) on brain-derived neurotrophic factor and low-grade
         inflammation among fibromyalgia patients: A randomized
         controlled trial." *Scientific Reports,* 2019; 9(1), 1-14. DOI:
         10.1038/s41598-019-52260-z

(7).   Herold, T; Jurinovic, V; Arnreich, C; Lipworth, B J; Hellmuth, J
         C; von Bergwelt-Baildon, M; Klein, M; Weinberger, T. "Elevated
         levels of IL-6 and CRP predict the need for mechanical
         ventilation in COVID-19." *The Journal of Allergy and Clinical
         Immunology,* 2020; 146(1), 128-136.e4. DOI: 10.1016/j.
         jaci.2020.05.008

(8).   Liu, F; Li, L; Xu, M; Wu, J; Luo, D; Zhu, Y; Li, B; Song, X; Zhou,
         X. "Prognostic value of interleukin-6, C-reactive protein, and
         procalcitonin in patients with COVID-19." *Journal of Clinical
         Virology,* 2020; 127, 104370. DOI: 10.1016/j.jcv.2020.104370

(9).   Pace, T; Negi, L T; Adame, D; Cole, S; Sivilli, T; Brown, T;
         Issa, M; Raison, C. "108. Effect of compassion meditation
         on autonomic, neuroendocrine and inflammatory pathway
         reactivity to psychosocial stress." *Brain, Behavior, and
         Immunity,* 2008; 22(4), 34. DOI: 10.1016/j.bbi.2008.04.110

(10).   Breines, J G; Thoma, M V; Gianferante, D; Hanlin, L; Chen, X;
         Rohleder, N. "Self-compassion as a predictor of interleukin-6
         response to acute psychosocial stress." *Brain, Behavior, and
         Immunity,* 2014; 37, 109-114. DOI: 10.1016/j.bbi.2013.11.006

(11).   Booij, S H; Bos, E H; Bouwmans, M E J; van Faassen, M; Kema,
         I P; Oldehinkel, A J; de Jonge, P. "Cortisol and alpha-Amylase
         Secretion Patterns between and within Depressed and Non-
         Depressed Individuals. *PloS One,* 2015; 10(7), e0131002. DOI:
         10.1371/journal.pone.0131002

(12).   Nater, U M; Rohleder, N. "Salivary alpha-amylase as a non-
         invasive biomarker for the sympathetic nervous system: current
         state of research." *Psychoneuroendocrinology,* 2009; 34(4), 486-
         496. DOI: 10.1016/j.psyneuen.2009.01.014

(13).   Neff, K D; Long, P; Knox, M C; Davidson, O; Kuchar, A;
        Costigan, A; Williamson, Z; Rohleder, N; Tóth-Király,
        I; Breines, J G. "The forest and the trees: Examining the
        association of self-compassion and its positive and negative
        components with psychological functioning." *Self and Identity*,
        2018; 17(6), 627-645. DOI: 10.1080/15298868.2018.1436587

(14).   Arch, J J; Brown, K W; Dean, D J; Landy, L N; Brown, K;
        Laudenslager, M L. "Self-compassion training modulates alpha-
        amylase, heart rate variability, and subjective responses to
        social evaluative threat in women." *Psychoneuroendocrinology*,
        2014; 42, 49-58.
        DOI: 10.1016/j.psyneuen.2013.12.018

(15).   Booij, S H, et al, 2015

(16).   Scannapieco, F A; Torres, G; Levine, M J. "Salivary alpha-
        amylase: role in dental plaque and caries formation." *Critical
        Reviews in Oral Biology and Medicine: An Official Publication
        of the American Association of Oral Biologists*, 1993; 4(3-4), 301-
        307. DOI: 10.1177/10454411930040030701

(17).   Scannapieco, F A; Bush, R B; Paju, S. "Associations
        Between Periodontal Disease and Risk for Atherosclerosis,
        Cardiovascular Disease, and Stroke. A Systematic Review."
        Annals of Periodontology, 2003; 8(1), 38-53. DOI: 10.1902/
        annals.2003.8.1.38

(18).   Ikeda, A; Steptoe, A; Brunner, E J; Maruyama, K; Tomooka, K;
        Kato, T; Miyoshi, N; Nishioka, S; Saito, I; Tanigawa, T. "Salivary
        Alpha-Amylase Activity in Relation to Cardiometabolic Status
        in Japanese Adults without History of Cardiovascular Disease."
        Journal of Atherosclerosis and Thrombosis, 2021; 28(8), 852-864.
        DOI: 10.5551/jat.53926

(19).   Pace, T W W; Negi, L T; Dodson-Lavelle, B; Ozawa-de Silva,
        B; Reddy, S D; Cole, S P; Danese, A; Craighead, L W; Raison, C
        L."Engagement with Cognitively-Based Compassion Training
        is associated with reduced salivary C-reactive protein from
        before to after training in foster care program adolescents."
        Psychoneuroendocrinology, 2013; 38(2), 294-299. DOI: 10.1016/j.
        psyneuen.2012.05.019

(20). Godoy, L C; Frankfurter, C; Cooper, M; Lay, C; Maunder, R; Farkouh, M E. "Association of Adverse Childhood Experiences With Cardiovascular Disease Later in Life: A Review." *JAMA Cardiology*, 2021; 6(2), 228-235. DOI: 10.1001/jamacardio.2020.6050

(21). Pace, T W W, et al., 2013

(22). Breines, J G; McInnis, C M; Kuras, Y I; Thoma, M V; Gianferante, D; Hanlin, L; Chen, X; Rohleder, N. Self-compassionate young adults show lower salivary alpha-amylase responses to repeated psychosocial stress." *Self and Identity*, 2015; 14(4), 390-402. DOI: 10.1080/15298868.2015.1005659

(23). Pace, T, et al., 2008

(24). Pace, T W W, et al., 2013

(25). Arch, J J, et al., 2014

(26). Hennein, R; Mew, E J; Lowe, S R. "Socio-ecological predictors of mental health outcomes among healthcare workers during the COVID-19 pandemic in the United States." *Plos One*, 2021; 6(2), e0246602. DOI:10.1371/journal.pone.0246602

(27). d'Ettorre, G; Ceccarelli, G; Santinelli, L; Vassalini, P; Innocenti, G P; Alessandri, F; Tarsitani, L. "Post-traumatic stress symptoms in healthcare workers dealing with the COVID-19 pandemic: A systematic review." *International Journal of Environmental Research and Public Health*, 2021; 18(2). DOI:10.3390/ijerph18020601

(28). Carmassi, C; Foghi, C; Dell'Oste, V; Cordone, A; Bertelloni, C A; Bui, E; Dell'Osso, L. "PTSD symptoms in healthcare workers facing the three coronavirus outbreaks: What can we expect after the COVID-19 pandemic." *Psychiatry Research*, 2020; 292, 113312. DOI:10.1016/j.psychres.2020.113312

CHAPTER SEVEN

(1). Condon, P; Desbordes, G; Miller, W B; DeSteno, D. "Meditation Increases Compassionate Responses to Suffering." *Psychological Science*, 2013; 24(10), 2125-2127. DOI: 10.1177/0956797613485603

(2). Kirby, J N. "Compassion interventions: The programmes, the evidence, and implications for research and practice." *Psychology and Psychotherapy*, 2017; 90(3), 432-455. DOI: 10.1111/papt.12104

CHAPTER EIGHT

(1). The Self-Compassion Scale (SCS), created by Dr. Kristen Neff. https://self-compassion.org/self-compassion-scales-for-researchers/

(2). Neff, K D. "The Self-Compassion Scale is a valid and theoretically coherent measure of self-compassion": Erratum. *Mindfulness*, 2016; 7(4), 1009. DOI: 10.1007/s12671-016-0560-6

(3). The Self-Compassion Scale—Short-Form (SCS-SF). https://self-compassion.org/self-compassion-scales-for-researchers/

(4). Pommier, E; Neff, K D; Tóth-Király, I. "The Development and Validation of the Compassion Scale." Assessment, 2020; 27(1), 21-39. DOI: 10.1177/1073191119874108

(5). The Compassion Scale (CS). https://self-compassion.org/self-compassion-scales-for-researchers/

(6). Martins, D; Nicholas, N A; Shaheen, M; Jones, L; Norris, K. "The development and evaluation of a compassion scale." *Journal of Health Care for the Poor and Underserved*, 2013; 24(3), 1235-1246. DOI: 10.1353/hpu.2013.0148

(7). Strauss, C; Lever Taylor, B; Gu, J; Kuyken, W; Baer, R; Jones, F; Cavanagh, K. "What is compassion and how can we measure it? A review of definitions and measures." *Clinical Psychology Review*, 2016; 47, 15-27. DOI: 10.1016/j.cpr.2016.05.004

(8). Lown, B A; Muncer, S J; Chadwick, R. "Can compassionate healthcare be measured? The Schwartz Center Compassionate Care Scale™." *Patient Education and Counseling*, 2016; 98(8), 1005-1010 DOI: 10.1016/j.pec.2015.03.019

(9). Strauss, C, et al., 2016

(10). Burnell, L. "Compassionate Care: Can it be Defined and Measured? The Development of the Compassionate Care Assessment Tool." *International Journal of Caring Sciences*, 2013; 6:2. http://internationaljournalofcaringsciences.org/docs/6.%20Burnell%20Compassionate%20Care%20Tool.pdf

(11). Strauss, C, et al., 2016

(12). Strauss, C, et al., 2016

(13). Gu, J; Baer, R; Cavanagh, K; Kuyken, W; Strauss, C. "Development and Psychometric Properties of the Sussex-Oxford Compassion Scales (SOCS)." Assessment, 2020; 27(1), 3-20. DOI: 10.1177/1073191119860911

(14). Gu, J, et al., 2020

CHAPTER NINE

(1). McKnight, D. *Tonglen meditation's effect on levels of compassion and self-compassion: A pilot study and instructional guide.* Thesis Completed as Part of the Upaya Buddhist Chaplaincy Training Program, 2012. https://www.upaya.org/uploads/pdfs/McKnightTonglenThesis.pdf

(2). Neff, Kristen. *Self-Compassion: Stop Beating Yourself Up and Leave Insecurity Behind.* William Morrow, 2011. ISBN-13: 978-0061733512

(3). Bach, D; Groesbeck, G; Stapleton, P; Sims, R; Blickheuser, K; Church, D. "Clinical EFT (Emotional Freedom Techniques) Improves Multiple Physiological Markers of Health." *Journal of Evidence-Based Integrative Medicine*, 2019; 24, 2515690X18823691. DOI: 10.1177/2515690X18823691

(4). The Compassion Project. https://thecompassionproject.com/

(5). Kirby, J N. "Compassion interventions: The programmes, the evidence, and implications for research and practice." *Psychology and Psychotherapy*, 2017; 90 (3), 432–455. DOI: 10.1111/papt.12104

(6).   Reddy, S D; Negi, L; Dodson-Lavelle, B; Ozawa-De Silva, B;
        Pace, T W W; Cole, S P; Raison, C L; Wilcoxon Craighead,
        L. "Cognitive-Based Compassion Training: A Promising
        Prevention Strategy for At-Risk Adolescents." *Journal
        of Child and Family Studies*, 2012; 22(2). DOI:10.1007/
        s10826-012-9571-7

(7).   Kirby, J N, et al., 2017

(8).   Gilbert, P. "The origins and nature of compassion-focused
        therapy." *British Journal of Clinical Psychology*, 2014; 53 (1),
        6–41. DOI: 10.1111/bjc.12043

(9).   Jazaieri, H; Jinpa, G T; McGonigal, K; Rosenberg, E L;
        Finkelstein, J; Simon-Thomas E; et al. "Enhancing compassion:
        A randomized controlled trial of a compassion cultivation
        training program." *Journal of Happiness Studies*, 2012; 14 (4),
        1113–1126. DOI: 10.1007/s10902-012-9373-z

(10).   The Center for Compassion and Altruism Research and
        Education (CCARE) at Stanford University. https://ccare.
        stanford.edu/

Acknowledgments

WHEN THINKING ABOUT whom to acknowledge, I wanted to write the name of every single person I have encountered in my life, because each person truly has been a part of my evolution. Since that is impossible, here is my best effort.

Each person I mention has given me strength and a belief that I can do this, and has shown me the power of compassion in their own way.

Thank you to my mother, Karen, for having the biggest heart of any human I have ever met. Ma, for loving me so fiercely. My Dads—Carl for being here now, and James for loving me sight unseen. Margarita, for being the embodiment of compassion. I would not be here without you all. My Godparents, Shirley and Bob, for being the lighthouse in the storm. My sisters, Chelsea and Emmy, you healed so much for me. Sara, for you, for bringing my sisters into this world, and for being Grandma Sara to George. My brother, C.D., for your protection, and for getting me through the summer of physics. C.D.'s wife, Charlotte, for loving my brother through it all. My entire maternal family of origin for teaching me lessons in love, forgiveness, and compassion. The Garza family for being my family when I felt alone. Dan and Judy Schweikert for being the best in-laws a woman could hope for.

Jeannie Ferrara, whose light is so bright I could do nothing but follow it. JJean J. Farnsworth, from Choco-cats to married with children, you've seen me at my best and worst thank you for loving me through all of it. I love you. Jeannette Contreras, for listening, sharing, and cleaning up my messes both in my home and my mind. Dr. Joyce Mikal-Flynn, you are a beacon of light; I am humbled and grateful for all the opportunities you give me.

My Saybrook besties, Phoebe and Silvia, who put up with my complaining and inspire me.

My dissertation committee: Dr. Cynthia Kerson (Saybrook University), for guiding me with your humanness and brilliant mind; and Dr. Rich Sherman (Saybrook University), for not letting me off the hook, like, ever. Dr. Inna Khazan (Harvard University), for being willing to share your HRV expertise with me.

Dr. Alexis Jennings, my time traveler twin, who encouraged me to write this book without fear.

Tarah Franklin, for being a beacon of love and faith.

My UCD clan, Barb Wiesner and John Graykoski (I sat between giants). Ingeborg Sammern, for reminding me I am never too old for roller skating. Patrick Guimond, for all the music and food and living your dream out loud (Spirit Oak, here we come)! Mama Phillips, I will always be your TPO.

My mom crew: Rose, Kim, and Rosie, y'all inspire me and keep me going in the thick of real life. To all My Nuggets, especially the OGs: Gio, Claire, Andrew, and Dane, I will always be your second mom. Our door is always open, forever. My truest bestie, Olive Portola. Cheryl and Naomi, for being the best big sisters on the street.

Sutter Medical Group, for giving me a place to practice, and especially Dr. Don Wreden and Dr. Max Barish-Wreden for always welcoming and inspiring me. Dr. Sabra Granovsky, I miss you every time I walk through those doors. Dr. J., for giving me my first solo compassion opportunity. Dr. P.T. Koenig, for my first Firestarter job. Dr. Steve Vilter, for embodying compassion at each shift. Dr. Lorraine Abate, for knowing the Camelot years with me. Dr. Tin Nguyen, for knowing proper lighting and music. May this book be bussin' no cap. Dr. Katie Askew, for allowing me to be me. Dr. Kathy Gouvea, for being more excited about this book than me and squats. Dr. Queena Dai, for displaying incredible patience that inspires me. Marina, Sue, Rose, Darla, Aarika, Mattie, Renisha, Atika, T, Fernando, Michelle, Lisa, and Crystal, for being the UC OGs and showing us all compassion. Together, you make it easy to put up with the difficulties of work, making it feel like play.

My Kaiser people: Dr. Mike Lawson and Dr. Mark Sheffield, for believing in me before I did. Gina Rossi, for my first research job and welding.

The Merrick Family. Ulrike, you love so beautifully.

My Stanford mentors, Neelama Eyres and Robert Cusick. Dr. James Doty, for creating a place where I found my purpose.

Monica Jansen, for being my best friend since we were twelve, and for all that followed.

Diana Dripps, for climbing in my head with me and pulling me out of it too.

The WorldChangers Media team, especially Stephen and Marie, thank you so much! Bryna, I will never be able to fully express my gratitude for your gifts and encouragement. This book wouldn't exist without you. Thank you.

All of my research participants: thank you for trusting me with your hair!

Karl, you are my everything. You are my safe place, my refuge, shelter from the storms. Your encyclopedic knowledge has come in handy on more than one occasion. Through the 4:00 a.m. writing sessions to the panic and overwhelm, you remained steady and strong, and I will never forget how lucky I am to have you in my life. I love my life when you are in it, and I love you.

George, you are my heart and soul. I love you. I wrote this book with the hope that I will leave this world a better place for you and the life you create as you grow. You remind me of how beautiful this world truly is, every day. I am so lucky to be your mom, and I am so proud of you. You are my favorite everything.

And finally, to anyone I have forgotten to mention here: please know that I am deeply grateful for your presence in my life in every shape and form, and that although my pen may forget today, my heart remembers, always.

About the Author

CATHERINE WERGIN SCHWEIKERT, PhD, MPH, PA-C, has practiced medicine for twenty-two years. She wrote *The Compassion Remedy* while earning her PhD in Applied Psychophysiology. She completed a year-long deep dive into applied compassion at Stanford University's Center for Compassion and Altruism and Research (CCARE); it was there that she developed a program for hospitals to apply the scientifically proven and research-based aspects of compassion.

Her intention, first and foremost, is to improve clinicians' grounded, compassionate bases so that they may be strong enough to help patients heal without giving away their vitality. Catherine is also a contributor to the Global Compassion Coalition.

She is currently bringing her message of pragmatic embodied compassion not only to hospitals but also universities, domestic violence women's groups, and the Veterans Administration through MetaHab© post-traumatic growth programs. She is open and excited to speak and teach for corporate or private engagements.

Learn more about Catherine's work and inquire about speaker booking at www.pragmaticcompassion.org.

About the Publisher

FOUNDED IN 2021 by Bryna Haynes, WorldChangers Media is a boutique publishing company focused on "Ideas for Impact." We know that great books change lives, topple outdated paradigms, and build movements. Our commitment is to deliver superior-quality transformational nonfiction by, and for, the next generation of thought leaders.

Ready to write and publish your book with us? Learn more at www.WorldChangers.Media.

WORLDCHANGERS
M E D I A

Printed in the USA
CPSIA information can be obtained
at www.ICGtesting.com
JSHW020707220923
48885JS00001B/38

9 781955 811378